# INTO
# THE UNKNOWN

# INTO THE UNKNOWN

## HUMAN EXPLORATION IN THE TRUE SPACE AGE

ELLENA HYEJI JOO

NEW DEGREE PRESS



INTO THE UNKNOWN

*Human Exploration in the True Space Age*

ISBN 978-1-63676-489-4 *Paperback*

978-1-63730-401-3 *Kindle Ebook*

978-1-63730-402-0 *Ebook*

*For my brother. Stay curious.*

# CONTENTS

## INTRODUCTION

# INTO THE UNKNOWN

*The surface of the Earth is the shore of the cosmic ocean. From it we have learned most of what we know. Recently, we have waded a little out to sea, enough to dampen our toes or, at most, wet our ankles. The water seems inviting.*

—CARL SAGAN, AUTHOR OF *COSMOS*

I'm in the cosmic water right now, alone, but happily curious. I'm anxious, but really excited for this adventure. I'm wondering if it's just me here when—oh, *hey you!* I know you! You're the one I heard so much about who, like me, often looks up at the sky and wonders what's out there. You've stepped into the water today by opening this book. Instead of stopping at your feet, I invite you to go deeper. Take a dive with me, and together, let's explore the unchartered depths of this universe.

Our first stop: Octomom.

Have you heard of Octomom? The mother who gave birth to eight children at once? No, not her. Although, I won't deny she is also a testament to the unforeseen nature of this universe.

I'm talking about the *real* octomom—the octopus mom.

It's the summer of 2007. Born and raised near the Californian beach, marine researcher Bruce Robison has always been deeply curious about sea life. Through his work, he lets himself go deeper with each dive, as he researches sea life on a ship off the Monterey Canyon coast (McEwan, 2020).

On routine checks of sea life, Bruce's team drops a robot submarine a mile below the ocean's surface. Each time, Bruce is in awe of the endless depth of the ocean and the darkness illuminated by mere sparks of light. It's the light the sea creatures generate themselves, light that proves there is life this far below our familiar world.

One day, Bruce notices a purple-gray blob perched on a rock. He zooms in using the submarine's camera and realizes it's an octopus. The deep-sea octopus is apparently brooding, a practice of incubating eggs common for female octopuses. During this period, octopodes avoid eating or moving except to protect their eggs from predators until they hatch. He gets close enough to count exactly 160 eggs this octopus is guarding. Thinking it's a neat discovery, Bruce notes her distinct scar and moves along to finish exploring the rest of the area.

A few months later, Bruce and his team return to the coast for another routine check of sea life. In a moment of curiosity after the routine checks end early, Bruce navigates the robot submarine to the rock where he observed the octopus. To his surprise, it is still brooding in the same spot.

This octopus has broken the world record for a brooding period for all known octopuses. Frequently researched shallow water octopodes brood for a month, but the observations from land don't readily apply to the deep sea where scientists know little about the sea life (McEwan, 2020). This octopus has broken the known record not by days, but *months*. He counts the eggs, wary that predators swarming this part of the ocean could have eaten many of them. He releases a sigh of relief when he still gets 160. *Good job, Octomom,* he decides to call her.

Bruce returns every few months to Octomom, holding his breath, but there she is always, still brooding at the same rock on the same spot. Each time, he wonders if she has finally finished brooding or if predators have eaten her or her eggs. *This is the last time she's going to be here,* he thinks after every visit (Creighton, 2014). Yet she is always there the next time he visits, awaiting him to disprove his concerns.

Despite his wonder at her resilience, he can't help noticing Octomom looks increasingly thinner, her skin looser and paler. Several times, he notices crab carcasses scattered around her. They are the aftermath of her battles; she has fought to protect her eggs from predators. Every time, Bruce counts 160 eggs.

A full year passes. Bruce notices Octomom's eyes are filmy and opaque, like she has cataracts. Despite knowing octopuses starve while brooding, Bruce can't help but break off a crab leg using the robotic arm and try to feed her frail body. He tries this several times, but she refuses to eat.

Two years, three years, and finally, four years pass.

On land, Barack Obama becomes the president of the United States. Apple releases the first iPhone. Michael Jackson dies. The economy crashes. Human history continues to morph from one significant event to another, and just a mile below it all, Octomom has not moved an inch. Even after his now regular visits, Bruce thinks about Octomom as he goes through his daily life—washing his car, buying milk, or watching the news. After all the years he has spent studying and spending time with her, Bruce is fond of her. He misses her on land.

At the four-and-a-half-year mark, Bruce returns to Octomom's rock for the eighteenth time, expecting her to once again welcome him back with all 160 of her eggs. But she is gone. Instead, empty egg cases litter where she had lain. His mind jumps to the worst-case scenario. *Oh no, no, no . . .* That's when he notices that around the rock, baby octopuses are floating around.

Octomom's sudden disappearance stuns Bruce, and he gradually realizes she has successfully brooded only for some scavenger to consume her. He is overwhelmed with sadness and pride. He imagines her last moments. Aged with her cataracts, she was trying to blindly watch over her children. She was feeling them and guarding them with her entire body.

He releases a long-held breath and thinks, *Right. Okay, relax Mom. It's over. You did—you did your job* (McEwan, 2020).

Octomom set a new record as the longest living octopus as well as the longest brooding period record for all life on planet Earth. She will forever mark the hall of fame. In an interview with Radiolab NYC in 2020, thirteen years after he discovered Octomom, Bruce expresses he still remembers her fondly and not merely for her scientific significance. Outside of his duty as a marine researcher, Bruce felt a deep connection.

The deep-sea diver recalls the moments he discovered Octomom's ultimate sacrifice for her children. "I was relieved for her that all that effort, all that enduring and dedication was over. But at the same time, I was disappointed I wasn't going to see her again. I was fond of her" (California, 2014). Finally, Bruce shares that Octomom taught him a greater lesson on our perceptions on life, "We tend to think of parental care only in higher life-forms, but here's a parent who is going all out to ensure the survival of her offspring" (Creighton, 2014). He learned it's wrong to believe no life is as special, as civilized, as *human,* as our own.

When we talk about alien encounters, we think of science fiction, but Bruce's story is just one example of an alien encounter right here on Earth.

Deep-sea life, 200 meters or 656 feet below the surface of the water where light from the sun doesn't reach, composes the overwhelming majority (a staggering 90 percent) of sea life, yet to this day, these creatures are a mystery to marine biologists. Bruce's discovery and others like it prove even on Earth, we discover species alien to us, and amazingly, we can bond with them.

But more often, we respond to otherness with hostility and defensiveness rather than curiosity, open-mindedness, and empathy, as Bruce did with Octomom. Unfortunately, Bruce's story has uglier versions. When we allow ourselves to go deeper, further *into the unknown*, the consequences aren't always positive. Examples abound, such as European explorers' historical use of violence, slavery, and colonization against innocent people they considered less civilized. Even today, we label people and lives we don't identify with as "alien," "foreign," or "strange."

Scientists argue in this ineffably vast universe, we may not be the only intelligent beings. We may not even be the only intelligent beings in our own solar system (Gareth, 2020). The "circumstellar habitable zone," also known as the Goldilocks Zone after the children's tale "Goldilocks and the Three Bears" for its "just right-ness," is a range of orbits in which planets could have liquid water on their surfaces and potentially support intelligent life. Venus and Mars are in the Goldilocks Zone and could have at one point sustained intelligent life or could contain intelligent life we do not know of yet. Discoveries such as the Goldilocks Zone bring us one step closer to understanding the likelihood of intelligent life in our proximity. Just earlier in 2021, NASA's drone *Ingenuity* became the first human-controlled flight to Mars. We can now *fly* to planets in the Goldilocks Zone.

But the closer we get to discovering aliens, the more urgent it is we discuss what that actually means. Given humanity's complicated track record on encountering "alien" life on our own planet, we are in desperate need for a revision in our mind-set for encountering alien life. Even if the probability of meeting aliens during our lifetime is small, it is a probability worth considering—what will we do when aliens arrive? As long as the probability exists, it is a question we must prepare to answer. How we respond to this scenario could change the course of this universe as we know it and transform human history.

We are far from predicting what life-forms the intelligent extraterrestrials will embody or what purpose they will have in interacting with us. For alien encounters, we likely will not know when or where they will arrive, nor what they will be like. But as Bruce's serendipitous encounter with Octomom shows, until we meet the aliens personally, we won't know if we can create a bond with them. We might have more in common than we think.

I have (almost) survived four years of studying foreign service in college and harbored a question I thought my peers and professors would find ludicrous: How does foreign service work when it meets something truly foreign, like intelligent beings from outer space?

I knew this was a crazy question, but I couldn't let it go. I rarely feel deep gratitude for the current state of politics and foreign service. When I think of space, it is an infinite source of inspiration. Space has always been humanity's purest source of curiosity, infinite possibility, and a testament to our power in exploration, connection, and compassion. Following our curiosity like Bruce did, even if it's farfetched or an unlikely outcome, can lead to huge discoveries and breakthroughs.

If you're like me and you question what lies ahead for humanity's future in the universe, you've probably embarked upon a few space operas, science fiction novels, and movies set in space that attempted to answer this question. They disappointed you, discouraged you, or terrified you into wetting your pants imagining an alien invasion scenario. But I want to offer a different future. I argue we need to develop the ability to think differently. We need to prepare for diplomacy with aliens.

From unpacking our fear of aliens, outlining principles for positive alien engagement, and exploring how to build a framework for alien encounters according to governments, scientists, anthropologists, space junkies, and more, this book will begin the conversation of how to stay positive as we enter the intergalactic age. It'll be a journey of overcoming our previous patterns of thought and engagement, and simultaneously, it'll be a journey of rediscovering humanity.

Don't forget Bruce's story. Don't forget your own power to connect. Don't be afraid to develop the capacity to understand things foreign or alien to you. In today's dog-eat-dog world of politics, I want to prove we *can* build a framework for thinking about and practicing diplomacy in a collaborative, empathetic way, both on Earth and in outer space.

We have waded just a little out to sea, deep enough to dampen our toes, wet our ankles, and even deep enough to meet a mother who has fiercely protected 160 babies with her life—a mother who reminded us humanity and wonder can be found by humankind if one dares to dive deep enough to seek it. Doesn't the water seem inviting? Together, let's dive into the unknown. Let's explore what the future can hold for humanity in the True Space Age.

# PART 1

# LIFT OFF

## CHAPTER 1

# ALIENS ON EARTH

On the first day of a class I took my junior year called US Foreign Policy in the Arab Middle East, I stepped foot in the classroom and stepped right back out.

Once I checked with my syllabus that I was indeed in the right room, I went back inside. I was uncertain if I was in the right classroom because I'd never been in an undergraduate class with so many people who had beards. I realized soon after sitting myself down and class beginning that the course was open to both undergraduates and graduate students. *Ah,* I thought, *so most people in my class are graduate students*—hence their years of beard-groomed wisdom.

Even more fascinating than the number of older students was that my classmates came from a great diversity of backgrounds. In the class of seven, there were students from Cuba, Turkey, Palestine, and France. My professor explained to us he was from Tunisia. Who knew beards were so universally popular?

There were just two American students in the class, one of whom was a student named Andrew who shared on the first day he is a US Navy SEAL sniper and had been recently deployed in combat zones in the Middle East (and yes, he also had a great beard). Given his background, he added an interesting point of view to the discussion, one established on patriotism and a deep respect for authority.

I took this class reluctantly, as it was one of the last open courses to fulfill a requirement for my international politics and foreign policy major. I knew nothing about the Arab Middle East, or the Middle East in general. I must confess, my only understanding of the region was from the media, mainstream news, or movies. Even more embarrassing to confess is one of my favorite Disney movies growing up, *Aladdin*, was often what I associated with the Arab region (Clements, 1992).

One day before class started, the room was engaged in small talk. Toni, who was from Cuba, shared his dinner plans while Zara from Palestine mentioned she was struggling to catch up on readings. Andrew casually dropped the fact that he was going to go home to his wife after class.

Bewildered, I blurted, "Wow, you're married? I forget graduate students have entire lives outside of school."

To my surprise, Andrew replied, "Oh, I'm no graduate student. I'm only in my third year in college."

I couldn't believe this person was in my grade, but then again, I probably seemed odd to him with my baby face and ill-fitting hoodie I threw on to cover the pajamas I rolled out of bed in. This brief conversation felt about as smooth as nails on a chalkboard, and I wanted to crawl back to my bed from the shame. Married, a Navy SEAL sniper, and an undergraduate, Andrew was profoundly different from me, like many people in the classroom were. This class had the most diverse demographic of people I'd ever been in, and that always reminded me I had a lot to learn from our conversations, particularly on the topic of our course.

Unlike the light banter, the atmosphere in the room quickly became heavy as class began.

We were discussing the lethality of "checkpoints" in the West Bank, where Israeli soldiers in heavily Palestinian-populated areas police pedestrians who try to pass. We learned about this controversy to discuss whether Israel Defense Forces were justified using their weapons on civilians. That afternoon was especially difficult for Zara, who was from Palestine. Not only was the overarching Israel-Palestine conflict deeply personal to Zara but the video footage our professor played at a certain checkpoint was familiar to her because it was at a location close to her home.

The video was short, around thirty seconds long, but its content from two years ago has not left my memory: a Palestinian woman shot to death by the IDF at the checkpoint for allegedly carrying a knife and failing to obey orders to stop (The Observers-France, 2019).

The video ended, and no one spoke. I glanced apprehensively at Zara, who looked visibly upset. When the professor finally spoke, he shared that the video was footage from the day before our class, uploaded on September 18, 2019. The class fell silent again. Sitting in class on a warm afternoon in Washington, DC, the video of death from across the world almost seemed chillingly unreal. I felt unsure of what to say.

Zara broke the silence first, "I just want to say this: It's crazy to me where she got shot is where I've stood hundreds of times, where I will again have to stand when I return home."

As Zara spoke, the video became more real to me. I felt deeply sorry for her and saddened because the violence was so close to her home. I could tell people in class were staying quiet to allow Zara the space to talk. But unexpectedly, Andrew responded at length, "Well, I don't think we should jump to conclusions that the woman is innocent. We don't know what she was doing outside of the thirty-second window of the video footage. Anything could have happened that made the soldiers shoot. Especially given they were following orders or responding to a more immediate threat unknown to us."

As the guy who sat next to her talked on, Zara's face clouded over in hurt. The professor interrupted Andrew, "Let's allow Zara to finish her thought."

But Andrew spoke over his interjections. "I'm a Navy SEAL sniper, and I've been in their shoes before. All I want to say is it's not an easy position to be in."

The rest of the class began to take sides. While the professor tried to calm us down and mediate our conversation, he made it clear whose side he was arguing for; the video had hit close to home for him as well as a refugee of authoritarian violence in Tunisia.

After class that day, I couldn't help but think about what Andrew said in response to Zara's thoughts. I had taken Zara's side, but I knew Andrew had simply shared his true feelings from experience as a sniper, which none of us could fully relate to. At the same time, Andrew seemed defensive, as if he felt personally targeted. But none of us, not even Zara, had accused him of anything. I wondered if Andrew was not just speaking to Zara or the rest of our class, but in fact speaking to himself to grapple with and justify the violence he was familiar with, that he had participated in only a few months ago.

Many more times in class, Andrew would impulsively defend the actions of America and other Western nations even when the historical context justified questioning these policies. I grew increasingly frustrated by his comments and didn't understand how he refused to see the story holistically, including the perspectives of the Palestinians, Egyptians, or Iranians.

I asked our professor one day during office hours about what he thought about our class.

He said, "It's all too familiar to me. A lot of students in our class are comfortable with a picture of the Middle East as an exotic place or a place of villains, filled with barbaric gangsters, turbans, and deserts. My job is to humanize the people and history of the Middle East to these students."

I felt guilty by what he said because I knew when I took this class, I also had preconceived notions of what the "Arab Middle East" would look like. I thought back to *Aladdin* and its opening number "Arabian Nights," whose original lyrics included the word "barbaric" and faced accusations of racism (Menken, 1992). Yet, its altered lyrics after the backlash refused to remove the word "barbaric" (Frook, 1993). At a young age, I would obliviously sing along with little thought about how the lyrics dehumanized the Arab people.

During the semester, I would look back to moments in my life when I had thought about the fact that countless movies I enjoyed had Arab villains or when I would dismiss checking on the Middle Eastern news, brushing it off as fundamentally chaotic. I know now I was plainly being racist without understanding how I was categorizing an entire region of people as less important and less human than I was.

We make sense of people we don't understand or have never met in two common ways: through alienation or dehumanization. Alienation creates distance between different groups, while dehumanization makes each group view the other as less than human. This is how I see it: if alienation pushes people away, dehumanization pushes people below by turning people subhuman.

I thought long about the professor's last comment and how his class was purposefully designed to "humanize" people who were already unquestionably human. I wondered if other classmates also had a different understanding of the Arab Middle East prior to class or harmful stereotypes they had internalized, as I had.

Chris, a student from New Jersey (the other American student), shared with me that after graduating college, this class was one of the most memorable from his time at Georgetown.

"This class gave me the tool kit to talk about issues with more nuance and sensitivity than I did before." He explained growing up in an area where most of his friends and neighbors had visited or lived in Israel, he rarely thought twice about the Palestinians nor the broader Arab region as the "victims" of the conflict. More so, he was always convinced there was only one narrative to the story.

When we do not see other groups as our equals or see them as "barbaric," primitive, and less than human, we are more likely to use violence against them. Not shockingly, dehumanization and desensitization have been deeply integrated into combat training, especially for the American military. A study by law enforcement trainer and retired US lieutenant colonel Dave Grossman has shown America is more effective in training soldiers to shoot to kill over time. The firing rate of American soldiers who shot to kill was less than 30 percent in WWII, which grew to 55 percent in the Korean War and rose to 90 percent in the Vietnam War (Grossman, 2009). It has been shown seeing targets as less than human makes it easier to justify using violence.

In the twenty-first century, the US military is evolving its tactics with the aid of technology, specifically with violent, graphic video games. No longer training by shooting at bull's-eyes, the military trains soldiers to shoot at three-dimensional characters who resemble human targets as much as possible. Some of these targets are overtly Muslim "enemies" and speak Arabic and wear keffiyehs (Lee, 2016).

One game rife with shooting targets that speak Arabic and wear keffiyehs is the globally popular *Call of Duty: Modern*

*Warfare*, a game American soldiers also used for first-person shooter training. Rami Ismail, an Arab and Muslim video game developer who speaks out on the lack of diversity in video games, described *Modern Warfare* as a shameless mission of "Shoot all the Arabs." He describes how the game follows the idea that "Muslim blood is the cheapest in the world" (Lee, 2016). Most soldiers in active duty who have experienced video game training have equated their experience to "brainwashing" while admitting the games do not prepare them for the battlefield (Romaniuk, 2017), One soldier admitted, "When I really think of the government seeing that as training, I laugh, but I also feel a bit uneasy" (Romaniuk, 2017). Troublingly, psychologists were able to use brain scans to show playing violent video games has the potential to desensitize players to real-life violence and the suffering of others (Romaniuk, 2017). Furthermore, stereotypes we internalize from media and entertainment can be difficult to unlearn, especially when validated by governments as military training, which *rarely go questioned.*

On the last day of the semester, we were sharing what parts of the class we had most enjoyed while chomping on some falafel and tabouleh the professor had graciously prepared for us.

When it became Andrew's turn, for the first time, he seemed shy to speak up: "I've shot people before. I had to look through the lens of my gun and actively forget about who it was I'm shooting at. This class made me question the practices and beliefs I've had."

Andrew's final comment reverberated with me. Despite our differences, we were both going through the same journey of learning. We were seeing our mistakes in dehumanizing people we didn't see as equal, whether it was rooted in Disney films, video games, or military training.

It was clear throughout the rest of the semester, as we learned about the history, culture, and people of nations in the Middle East, Andrew stopped speaking merely as an American sniper. His contributions were often ardent, almost emotional, and he spoke about each topic foremost as a *human being*. Andrew and I, and perhaps a lot more people in the class, were learning how to connect to people we had thought were so different from us, that we had learned to see as alien.

Our professor clasped Andrew's hand as we were leaving class for the last time.

"Thank you, professor," I heard him say.

Andrew is an example of how dismantling our learned dehumanization can improve our ability to relate to others. There are many other examples, some we often take for granted. Historically, humans have incorporated this practice to justify enslaving, murdering, and colonizing unfamiliar communities. A poignant example is when Europeans came to Africa in the nineteenth century during the Scramble for Africa, which would lead to a near-total colonization of the continent (Gates, 2021). Europeans saw Africa as a continent of less developed, subhuman people who were too different from them.

The vocabulary of colonization is very similar to the lyrics to *Aladdin*'s "Arabian Nights" (Menken, 1992). During the

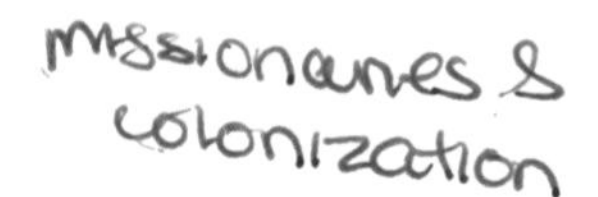


exploration period in the nineteenth century preliminary to colonization, Robert Moffat, a Scottish Congregationalist missionary to Africa, recorded the South Africans he met as "savage" (Mann, 2019). Henry Morton Stanley recorded his encounters with Congolese Africans as "undeveloped" and "inexperienced" (Thomas, 1971). Finally, British missionary Thomas Morgan Thomas published a book called *Eleven Years in Central South Africa*, denoting Africans he met in Inyathi, a village in Matabeleland, as "primitive" (Wallis, 1945). These nineteenth-century explorers' and colonizers' primary accounts are rampant with phrases that dehumanize Africans by describing Africans' behaviors as primordial while picturing their intellects as incapable of morality or sympathy. Such records are disturbing, particularly given how much the missionaries were dependent on the locals to provide them with food, shelter, and even act as personal translators and guides. Soon after these missionaries' explorations, they would facilitate Europeans' colonization of Africa, leading the way for some 12.5 million men, women, and children of African descent to be forced into the transatlantic slave trade for more than three hundred years (Mintz, 2021).

European colonizers simultaneously alienated and dehumanized the people they met in Africa. It is well known this pattern repeats throughout history across the globe: European dehumanization of Indigenous people in the Americas, Nazi dehumanization of Jewish people in the Holocaust, the Japanese colonization of Taiwan, Korea, Mongolia, parts of China and Russia, and much more. Colonization, enslavement, dehumanization, and alienation mar the human race's past and present. What was the trigger in the earliest encounters? Difference in languages? Variance in governing structures?

Difference in diets? Religious tensions? Or simply unfamiliarity with people who looked different?

Anthropologist Kathryn Denning, who is a senior researcher for SETI, the Search for Extraterrestrial Intelligence Institute, believes the fundamental answer lies in our "systematic prejudice" and failure "to recognize other people's agency, signatures, or existence" (Denning, 2018). She applies her answer to "alien" encounters among the human race when we have faced people or situations difficult to imagine or recognize. When faced with difference, no matter how amazing or ingenious, humanity has often assumed superiority.

One example she provides is of the indigenous societies of the Americas, particularly in Mexico. The Spanish colonists built a church atop the Great Pyramid of Cholula (three times larger than the Great Pyramid of Giza in Egypt and the largest pyramid on the planet) believing it was just a hill, as the pyramid was covered by the overgrown nature. Their belief persisted from the 1500s until the 1900s. For centuries, Europeans refused to believe in the indigenous people's agency, resource use, and management. They pictured the lands they "discovered" as virgin wilderness and believed the people were too primal and barbaric to properly utilize it themselves. Denning describes this as a "prejudice against recognizing the complexity and success of the indigenous societies" (Denning 2018). Their story shows prejudice is hard to fight, especially when persisted for a long period even in the face of stark evidence proving we are wrong.

In more recent history, we still observe alienation and dehumanization. For one, hostile climates against immigrants and foreigners have often marked them as aliens, sometimes literally. One notable law in American history is the California Alien Land Law of 1913, which targeted immigrants from China, India, Japan, and Korea by referring to them literally as "aliens" and prohibiting them from owning land or homes. The intention of the act was to create inhospitable environments in the United States for the "aliens" and discourage immigration from Asia (Ichioka, 1984). More often, Europeans migrating to America were referred to as "European immigrants," while Asians with the same intentions were referred to as "Oriental aliens" (Olin, 1966). Stanford University research finds this connection was quite literally related to seeing Asians as extraterrestrials. It writes, "the alien stands as a convenient metaphor for the experiences of Asian Americans, which range from the extraterrestrial being who seems to speak in a strange, yet familiar, accented English to the migrant subject excluded from legislative enfranchisement" (Sohn, 2008).

Even more recently, President Trump referred to immigrants as "animals" in a White House meeting in 2018. He stated, "You wouldn't believe how bad these people are," referring to immigrants. He followed by saying, "These aren't people, these are animals, and we're taking them out of the country at a level and at a rate that's never happened before" (Davis, 2018). Trump is one of many American politicians over the generations who have dehumanized the people they see as threatening or inferior. Given that seeing a group as less than human increases the risk of violence, these attitudes are putting people's lives in danger.

When we face actual aliens—not Asian immigrants or refugees fleeing civil wars, but truly extraterrestrial aliens—we'll be doomed by sticking to our usual tactics of alienation and dehumanization. Because if we're sorry in hindsight for colonization, Islamophobia, genocide, racism, and other ways we've facilitated violence upon each other, we can't risk being sorry by instigating a war with aliens. Humans might end up extinct, and it'll be too late to say sorry.

The key to breaking the cycle may lie in fighting our prejudice, according to Denning. Not letting alienation and dehumanization prevail in human history may begin with expanding our perspective and our capacity to humanize, empathize, and connect. Denning argues it is difficult to do this, especially when it comes to connecting with real aliens, extraterrestrial aliens. She notes that even anthropologists in the field who study human subjects by immersing themselves as much as possible in other's shoes don't truly become that subject any more than a human can truly become the alien (Denning, 2018). There's a limit to how much we can empathize. However, Denning states empathy is a skill we can learn to grow and is crucial to preparing for peace with aliens. She writes, "That process of immersion in another world, of striving to experience it as the Other does, is nonetheless generative" and will guide us in the search for extraterrestrial intelligence (Denning, 2018).

In fact, many studies show diversity in neighborhoods, classrooms, and exposure to differences on a daily level can contribute to greater tolerance, fair-mindedness, and openness to diverse settings. One study even shows multicultural exposure specifically "reduces biases toward the different others" (Chao, Kung, Yao 2015). Inclusive changes in our own environments can help us better prepare for when diversity takes on a whole new meaning.

We need to start small. Before we address the greater unknown, we need to inspect our own cognitive biases and systematic prejudices on a human-to-human level. We need to begin with alienation among ourselves, our inclination to limit our identity and weaponize our differences. We need to begin with dehumanization, our inclination to belittle and conquer one another.

Alienation and dehumanization are two sides of the same coin. When alienating, we push out and exclude, and when dehumanizing, we push down and degrade. One can easily turn to the other. This is how my friend simply summed it up: "Alienation is an instinctual, defensive recoil against when we feel threatened by a difference or an 'unknown.' Dehumanization, on the other hand, is more processed, more tactical; we have moved past the immediate shock of encountering something different, and even if it is a defensive strategy to explain the differences between us, we concluded that we must be superior in all of our differences." The persistence of both practices in humanity argues we are stubborn to respect only what we see as human and what we can relate to.

But we can learn to fight alienation and dehumanization and educate ourselves of our own biases as Andrew and I did in our class. Exposure to diversity, encouraging curiosity and learning, and having open, honest discussions about our differences can bring us together and prepare us for aliens.

While it's daunting to face our own biases and our own mistakes, self-awareness is the most practical and crucial first step to facing the unknown.

**CHAPTER 2**

# ESCAPING ANTHROPOCENTRISM

Hands up if you like puppies. Ah, I see we both have our hands up. The day puppies become political is the day I depart from this planet. Now, I want you to imagine a life without puppies. I'm not talking about a life where you regretfully chose the cat or the goldfish over the dog, but an actual world, a planet Earth, without dogs ever, period.

Kind of dark, right?

Dogs are one of the greatest gifts to life, and this is coming from a girl who has gone to the ER twice for her severe dog allergies. Even having almost died from them, I still love them and will continue to choose dog videos over a full night of sleep.

I want us to appreciate dogs, not just because they are addictively adorable, furry, and loyal but because studies by evolutionary scientists claim without dogs, us *Homo sapiens* may have never existed. You heard that right. Dogs may be the only reason we have evolved as *Homo sapiens* and supplanted *Homo neanderthalensis* in caveman time (Shipman, 2017). From tens of thousands of years ago, dogs' intelligence and sociality have enormously increased our hunting efficiency and survival in difficult environments, enabling our geographical expansion (Denning, 2018). Cute *and* crucial to our survival, dogs are gifts that just keep on giving.

Dogs are not the only animals that have played key roles in our timeline. Horses are heavily credited for shaping how the modern world thinks, including influencing language and communication skills we use today. One anthropologist credits the origins of the English language to the domestication of horses, which allowed for the spread of Proto-Indo-European language (Anthony, 2010). While horses and linguistics may seem unrelated, it makes a lot of sense. The first people to master riding horses were able to combine wagons and horses, allowing them to conquer massive amounts of territory across Europe and Asia and spread their culture and language (Anthony, 2010).

Without dogs or horses, I would not have the language to write this book nor could I be alive right now. I dedicate this book to all the pups and ponies out there continuing their hard work of evolving humankind. It's a hard job.

Scientists call key species to human survival such as dogs or horses our "co-evolutionary companions." While the role of canines and horses is widely recognized by evolutionary scientists, some have argued the list of life that has helped Homo sapiens' longevity and dominance can include pretty much every living thing on our planet, and it makes sense. Would we have persisted to become a globally dominant, technologically sophisticated species without whale oil to illuminate lamps for scholarly works? Or forests to burn to forge metal? Or without fossil fuels, which Denning calls "the legacy of ancient ecosystems?" (Denning, 2018).

This view questions anthropocentrism, the belief Homo sapiens single-handedly achieved our position as apex predators (Denning, 2018). Yes, it's powerful to think we are an exceptional, predestined species, but as anthropologist Denning puts it, we stand on the shoulders of giants, most of whom are not human (Denning, 2018).

Anthropocentrism projects into space. Anthropocentric views claim humans are the most significant entity of—or even the only intelligent entity in—the universe. We desperately need to escape anthropocentrism; we need to integrate a more holistic model of viewing our planet and our universe. Without recognition of our potential allies in outer space, we risk doing what our anthropocentric minds have done to our allies on Earth: we kill them, cook them, endanger them, or wage war on them, rashly thinking we can survive without them or rashly fearing they pose a threat to our survival. Yet we would be fools to not recognize we desperately need our allies.

In 2009, a movie about a struggle between an evil mining conglomerate and an indigenous tribe set a new record for the highest-grossing movie of all time. It was the movie *Avatar* (2009, Cameron). Set on fictional exoplanet Pandora, it is to this day one of the most successful movies in the genre of extraterrestrial life. For whatever reason, when I watched *Avatar* for the first time as a ten-year-old, I almost left the theater because I was so weirded out by alien sex, which according to *Avatar* is a magical moment when two aliens decide to braid each other's tails into one. I lost track of the movie's plot afterward.

Recently, I've successfully rewatched *Avatar* for the sake of research. Turns out, Avatar was dealing with a pretty important question on the future of alien encounters: is it possible to respect aliens as equals? Are we able to integrate into their communities peacefully? Most importantly, can we escape anthropocentrism out in space?

In *Avatar,* there are two teams: team human and team Na'vi, the indigenous community on Pandora. To make matters a little more complicated, team human is divided by two conflicting values. A few, such as an exobiologist who learns of the ecology of the planet and the culture of the indigenous species and the main character Jake Sully, are respectful of the Na'vi. On the other hand, the representatives of Earth (politicians) and the mining conglomerate (businessmen) fail to see the Na'vi as more than "savages" and inconveniences to their mining business. This difference is the central tension throughout the movie and what erupts into war between humans and the Na'vi.

These are my two biggest observations with *Avatar.* First, the humans fail to respect life on planet Pandora, and second, the humans act entitled as saviors to the Na'vi when in reality, the humans were the cause of their endangerment. It's a classic case of anthropocentrism, but also dehumanization.

The humans treat the Na'vi with no agency, as if they are incapable of caring for themselves, like children or animals. While on Earth, such treatment of others can be commonly attributed to dehumanization (as we saw in the previous chapter), in outer space, our juxtaposition with other sentient beings takes it a step further to anthropocentrism.

I was surprised by the ending of *Avatar*. For once, the humans did not prevail. The ending of the movie depicts humans tragically defeated by the Na'vi and serves as an appropriate warning against anthropocentrism. Primarily, it's a warning that underestimating extraterrestrials can mean unfortunate consequences for humans. Recognizing we aren't the most important or evolved beings out there can help us avoid this scenario in the first place.

*Avatar* is a movie, but it tells a story we can learn from. As we broaden our search for life in the universe and prepare for the real possibility of engaging with aliens, we need to practice escaping anthropocentrism, and here's why.

We need to escape anthropocentrism because underestimating other life-forms could have negative consequences for our research and survival. We cannot continue to explore space believing we are the only intelligent beings in the universe. Such a mind-set ensures we will be underprepared for the possibility aliens arrive on Earth or when we discover aliens out in space. We don't know what is really out there. When it comes to predicting extraterrestrial life, we don't know a single thing. We don't know what they look like, and we won't know their purpose for coming to Earth. If we don't get good at thinking beyond ourselves, we may end up jumping to false conclusions on what we think they want. If we are the ones who end up going to them, we *really* need to learn how to think beyond our self-interest. We need to avoid any scenario even remotely similar to *Avatar.*

I'm not saying we abandon our own survival needs when we land on someone else's planet, but the point is, we're landing on some other species's Earth. We should consider the ethics carefully before we jump to stealing their resources and screwing over their lives.

Anthropologist Pat Shipman declares we are "the most invasive species that has ever lived" (Shipman, 2017). Ouch, but it's true. Our capacity for invading and altering ecosystems and impacting other species is how we survived for so long on Earth. But it will ultimately be the impetus of our extinction. Just think of our situation today. Global warming and climate change threaten to make Earth inhabitable, and it has been our own doing. For so long, we thought we were above all other life on Earth, destroying it for our satisfaction, not thinking twice about how our actions would come back to haunt us. The Amazon Rainforest, the world's largest rainforest, reached its highest level of deforestation in 2020, and 80 percent was accounted for by cattle ranching (Yale, 2020). If we chose to equally prioritize the lives of other animals and plants to human development, we could have ensured a more positive future for our home.

Furthermore, we need to escape anthropocentrism because it isn't an accurate representation of how Homo sapiens have survived for this long. Yes, we have come this far by invading and altering ecosystems. But, as we've discussed, we have never been without allies who have played vitally important roles in our survival. Perhaps we could have come further had we adopted a mind-set earlier that was holistic and respectful of our planet's ecosystems. Anthropocentrism has not been a triumphant tactic, and it certainly will not be sustainable in our future. We are slowly adopting practices to conserve and support the ecosystems around us. One example is bee conservation projects. Honeybees pollinate approximately one hundred thirty agricultural crops in the United States, including fruit, fiber, nut, and vegetable crops, and their pollination adds approximately fourteen billion dollars annually to improved crop yield and quality (NASA, 2021). If we want to continue surviving, we need to keep our allies alive and, when it comes down to it, continue making allies out in space.

We're not there yet. So the first step is to escape anthropocentrism here on Earth, but how?

Professions that require objectively studying everything anthro-, such as anthropologists and archeologists, try to overcome anthropocentrism first and foremost (Kenrick, 2002). Understandably, when you are studying another human subject, you try your best to reduce your bias. This process of dissociation is anthropocentrism. When asked about this standard procedure, anthropologists and archeologists point to a surprisingly obvious first step we could all implement to overcome anthropocentrism: becoming less racist and ethnocentric (Boesch, 2010).

So now you know the most prevalent form of anthropocentrism is actually ethnocentrism. Archeologists and anthropologists describe how getting past ethnocentrism is important to more clearly see and understand people in other cultures. Being less ethnocentric is not just to observe others objectively, but to understand their subjectivities, to understand the way they themselves see their worlds (social, natural, and supernatural) and their own place and actions within them (Maybury Lewis, 1993; Augé, 1998). Because we each identify so strongly with our ethnicity or our race and given race is a politically charged identity in many parts of the world, it presents a barrier to our understanding of the human experience in the past and present.

As a matter of fact, *Avatar* shows ethnocentrism applies in space as well. Here's a crazy theory: Avatar is essentially a CGI-bedazzled *Pocahontas*, that animated Disney movie about the first colony in America where there was rampant racism and violence (Goldberg, 1995). You can replace Native Americans with giant blue people, set it on an exoplanet in 2154, invest two hundred million bucks on CGI, and *boom*, Disney has done it again. In both movies, the "settlers" or the non-indigenous are self-centered in their motives as they invade the local community with almost total disregard of the indigenous groups' agency, their use of the environment, and their lives. Both movies center on the tension between the indigenous and non-indigenous that leads to massacres instigated by both parties. Both movies try to tell an empowering, egalitarian story by showcasing the indigenous culture and community as beautiful and interesting, while still including this "white savior" trope and downplaying the impact of colonization. *Avatar* seems to show the power of the Na'vi by having them win against the human invasion, but they needed Jake to warn them about the danger and

plan a whole uprising for them while literally wearing a Na'vi skinsuit to do it. The overall message still ends up ethnocentric and anthropocentric despite the attempt to critique the previous patterns of white saviorhood in movies.

Vocabulary commonly used by colonialists to justify dehumanizing and murdering the indigenous people—"savages," "animals," "uncivilized"—is all there in both movies. *Avatar* is set in 2154. *Pocahontas* is set in 1607 (Goldberg, 1995). More than five hundred years apart, the movies mirror anthropocentrism in two different "alien" encounters. One movie is based on a true story, the story of the Algonquin Indians and the Virginia colony, and the other is futuristic science fiction. We know how centuries later, Pocahontas's story and many other stories of colonialism and imperialism left us with trauma and conflicts. If we overcome our ethnocentric and anthropocentric mind-sets, *Avatar* may never become a reality.

The famous writer-philosopher George Santayana said, "Those who cannot remember the past are condemned to repeat it" (Santayana, 2006). Others believe it doesn't matter if we try to spread the lessons of history. Billionaire Warren Buffet and eighteenth-century philosopher Georg Wilhelm Friedrich Hegel both said, "We learn from history that people do not learn from history" (Ilian, 2015). So many important people think peace and war are just the flow of human life, but let me be clear. For once, the big thoughtful people need to be wrong; history *cannot* repeat itself when it comes to aliens. The literal survival of the species and the trajectory of life as we know it may depend on it.

I want to take the claims of anthropologists one step further beyond ethnocentrism. Focusing on ethnocentrism as the sole example of anthropocentrism is, ironically, anthropocentric as well. Let's return to honeybees, puppies, and horses. Ecocentrism, the world view that applies equal intrinsic value on all living organisms, is crucial as well. Veganism, the practice to exclude, as far as is possible and practicable, all forms of exploitation of, and cruelty to, animals for food, clothing, or any other purpose, is a great example of an ecocentrism and non-anthropocentrism (Vegan Society, 2018). Meat eating today is the most extensive destruction of animals (Adams, 1990). From cattle ranching, which principally accounts for the death of the Amazon Rainforest, to the objectification and slaughter of 56 billion lives each year, 153.4 million each day, 6.4 million each hour, and 106,546 for our *appetite*, we can see how deeply rooted anthropocentrism is in our everyday life (Adams, 1990).

From meat eating, we can see how far we are willing to go to objectify another life because we believe the end justifies the means. We believe, as vegan-feminism activist Carol J. Adams writes in *The Sexual Politics of Meat*, "that the objectification of other beings is a necessary part of life and that violence can and should be masked" (Adams, 1990). The sad truth is we don't have to look further than our meals and pets to understand the extent of our anthropocentrism. We have come from needing our co-evolutionary companions such as dogs and horses for *our* survival to removing them from their natural habitats, caging them, breeding them, and forcing them to depend on us for *their* survival. Animal rights lawyers write, "When we talk about animal rights, we are talking primarily about *one* right: the right not to be property. The reason for this is that if animals matter morally—if animals are not just things—they *cannot* be property. If they are property, they can *only* be things." However "humanely" we treat animals, they are still subjected to objectifying treatment that, were humans involved, would be considered torture (Francione, 2016). Beyond the obligation to care for those domesticated animals who presently exist, we should work toward bringing no more into existence, regardless of their usefulness to humans. It's tricky to consider the reproductive rights of animals that are already pets, but it certainly enriches the discussion on how to recalibrate our relationship with animals, both domesticated and non-domesticated. To expand on my point in the previous chapter, to successfully evolve into a peaceful intergalactic species, we must strive to end all forms of dehumanization and alienation of all lives on our planet, for we are sure to project that habit in our ventures into the unknown.

Sadly, there is no guarantee that if we were to go out into space in the next few years, after discovering intelligent life, we would remember to take off our anthropocentric hats. We cannot completely escape anthropocentrism; we can't expect ourselves to think perfectly outside of our humanity and escape our centrism. We are only human, after all.

To more easily contextualize the human impact on the whole world, some geologists propose to define this anthropocentric period in recorded history as the Anthropocene Age. It's the age when humanity began to significantly alter this planet's atmosphere, from carbon dioxide emissions, global warming, habitat destruction, and extinction to large-scale natural resource extraction (Stromberg, 2013). Luz Lim, a geologist student from Amherst College, believes evaluating the Anthropocene Age may be the shift we need to take fighting against anthropocentrism one step further. She says, "We need to acknowledge ourselves within a context of time and space, and we must understand our actions not just as personal achievements for the sole entities that matter (as if we were in a vacuum), but as actions with contextual consequences." The Anthropocene Age is one great way to analyze our impact on this planet rather than just on the human story.

If we continue to explore the corners of the universe far and wide and wish to engage positively and peacefully with aliens, we must discipline ourselves ahead of time and be prepared with a less anthropocentric framework for the encounter. This discipline can begin by embracing ecocentrism and tackling ethnocentrism on Earth, meaning we finally have a reason to become decent human beings and embrace diversity! Jokes aside, we all have somewhere to begin and some part to play in preparing for extraterrestrial life, from evaluating the Anthropocene Age to acknowledging the role of dogs, horses, cows, and all life we cohabit Earth with to actively fighting our ethnic or racial prejudice.

## CHAPTER 3

# FEAR

This book is dedicated to my younger brother, a brilliantly curious, intelligent, and patient person who inspires me every day. Something few people know about him is he also has a lot of worries in his life. My family suspected it for years, but he was diagnosed with a form of severe OCD, a debilitating form of anxiety disorder, at the height of the pandemic in 2020. His OCD sequestered him in his room all day and night, and he continuously skipped meals and ignored our pleading knocks to talk. When I first started writing this book, it caused a breakthrough in our broken relationship. He, a space junkie and a huge *Star Trek*, *Star Wars*, and Marvel fan, felt confident in sharing his opinions as we discussed the future of planet Earth in the face of alien contact as the premise of my book.

Only the more we discussed and dived deeper into the research by astrobiologists, astrophysicists, and institutions dedicated to the search for extraterrestrial intelligent life (ETI), we realized how much fear is warranted in the face of the unknown. In the space movies my brother enjoys binging, humanity prevails unquestionably. After all, who would go to the cinema to watch the human species go *poof*? The research spoke loud and clear: the annihilation of humans could be a rather realistic portrayal of one possibility in a future with ETI.

For instance, when I got to chat with Dr. David Catling, the author of *Astrobiology: A Very Short Introduction,* he made it clear there is danger in searching for ETI. He said, "It can be argued the human species are simply unprepared for any form of multilateral unity in the unlikely scenario that we engage with ETI, and I believe it is true."

As I increasingly shared my research with my brother, I realized our talks were heightening his anxiety, not reducing it. He was no longer excited to discuss how we would kick any aliens' butts and get a happy ending like in his favorite Marvel movies, and instead he was deeply afraid of what could happen. His eyes lost the spark they carried when I first began sharing my discoveries, his voice more distant each time we talked. It seemed he lost interest in our conversations, but in truth, he was too afraid to think about space anymore, and eventually his door shut firmly once again.

I thought I had made a grave mistake and exacerbated his illness with our talks on space rather than the topics being a positive way for us to communicate. The worst thing you can do to a child suffering from OCD is provide the anxiety with more factors and situations that he has no control over, with one likely scenario of extreme disaster, arguably the worst possible disaster: the wiping out of human species. Not only that, I ruined his biggest passion—space and aliens—through my overtly realistic and pessimistic approach. Even if I wasn't the root cause of his OCD, I felt heavily responsible for instilling fear in him about the future of space. I needed to fix what I had done.

This book is that attempt; I want to help him unpack the fear one can have about our future in space, realize its scopes, come to terms with it, and move on. Maybe I can help you too.

Maybe, like my brother, you were once a young child who had wild imaginations about what lies ahead in humanity's future in space. Perhaps you also believed, like him, in our power of survival, our intelligence, and our ability to connect no matter what lies out there. Along the way, you were also disillusioned through the voice of reason who chided you to think more realistically. As Sigmund Freud once said, "The voice of reason is small, but very persistent." The voice came from everywhere—from your parents, your peers, and the news. So, you grew up.

People often tell us to "grow up" when we are overly optimistic; sometimes it seems adulthood is equated with more cynicism. A healthy dosage of fear is all the difference between a child and an adult, but blind fear alone does not an adult make.

Being able to practice active hope and self-awareness is equally important to adulthood and survival as fear. Even if the current science community still merits the possible danger of ETI, I believe there isn't a true dichotomy. We can still be hopeful of where our explorations lie in space and feel propelled to go further while being cautious about the ETI.

Fear doesn't need to ruin our hope for a positive future in space. I hope I can help unpack that fear and come to terms with it, and if I did my job right, help you feel a little more hopeful about what lies ahead.

* *

*Fear.* The unpleasant emotion caused by the perceived threat of danger. Fear is what has kept the human species alive for this long. Our primal fear ruled our lives for the best, keeping us away from what could eat us alive. Millions of years of evolution later, fear has become our least-respected instinct. It is actively trivialized, almost ignored; today, when you conquer something you fear, it means you're doing something right. Increasingly, we are encouraged to live as if we have no fear. TED Talks and self-help books preach that achieving greatness requires facing and overcoming your fear. In fact, there's a whole playlist for "How to Overcome Your Fears" on Ted.com (TED, 2020). While we think we are doing a great job, or at least the right job, when we overcome our irrational fears, what we don't realize is in some ways, fear has become a critical marketing tool in our consumerism.

One of the biggest reasons why we are trapped in a cycle of fear is because fear sells. Our fears and insecurities are the reasons why you buy certain products or watch certain shows. Businesses capitalize on our fears, especially ones that can attract a wide audience. One example is the fear of aliens. On the wide screen, we notice a recurring theme in international blockbusters: humanity united against a common threat. It's playing on our most primal fear: the fear of the extinction of our own species.

This narrative of aliens invading Earth began in popular culture by H. G. Wells and his book *War of the Worlds* published in 1897 (Catling, 2014). It is one of the earliest stories to detail conflict between humankind and an extraterrestrial race, a genre that would continuously increase in popularity even until today. What stands true then and now is most movies are mostly about us and our problems. For instance, *War of the Worlds* was a commentary on British imperialism and mirrored Victorian superstitions, fears, and prejudices. The *Star Trek* franchise, a timeless TV series and series of movies about conflict between mankind and ETI, shaped many popular opinions about aliens and carries plots that were also inspired by the politics of the day (Abrams, 2009; Roddenberry, 2008).

If we are afraid because the aliens may be like us, a species especially adept at destroying one another, we may transplant the worst parts of human behavior onto extraterrestrial intelligence. We're projecting ourselves out there. It's the height of anthropocentrism and a narrative that only says more about us than what may actually be out there.

Members of the IAA SETI (The International Academy of Astronautics Search for Extraterrestrial Intelligence) Permanent Committee, an international organization of scientists and academics dedicated to researching post-detection issues with ETI, have repeatedly told me aliens are the least of their worries. Anthropologist Kathryn Denning, for instance, said to me when asked about aliens, "I don't worry about aliens. I worry about human reactions to the idea of aliens. I worry about the way humans treat the life-forms we already know here on Earth." Senior SETI astronomer and past President of IAA SETI Permanent Committee, Dr. Seth Shostak, explained the current scientific thinking about actual aliens is that we don't coexist in time and space to be able to interact

face-to-face. Fear of aliens seems to be widespread among the uneducated public, while the experts in the frontline of the search for ETI are not concerned at all.

However, acclaimed scientists also drive our fear of aliens. Stephen Hawking famously said, as recently as 2016, "One day, we might receive a signal from a planet like this. But we should be wary of answering back. Meeting an advanced civilization could be like Native Americans encountering Columbus. That didn't turn out so well" (Bowerman, 2016). His quote was received with a lot of backlash from organizations such as SETI Institute because of the exact reaction it caused in his audience: panic and fear.

Various types of fear may actually hinder our progress in exploration and advancing the field of space. Often, strong negative emotions associated with a field can discourage new members from joining or public support. Dr. Catling shared the story of the tragedy of Martian canals and disillusionment's threat to scientific progress. In the nineteenth and early twentieth century, scientists stated they discovered signs of civilizations on Mars from the canals detected on telescopes, which received the attention of media worldwide. Unfortunately, improved technology later proved the canals to be optical illusions, and the media reported on the debacle and painted just as attentively, depicting the space community as embarrassing and mistrustful. Catling said, "This turn of events had a negative effect because people realized things they've been told had not been true." Consequently, Catling describes people avoided entering the fields of planetary science or planetary astronomy, while support and attention from the public dramatically reduced.

Here's a win for hope: optimism can drive increased interest in research and accumulate further realistic studies in the field. Catling believes the Space Race of the 1960s and 1970s and the optimistic frenzy surrounding the search for alien life helped recruit more aspiring academics into the field of astrobiology.

This lapse in interest only changed thanks to the Space Age in the late twentieth century, a period credited to top-down political support by the American government coupled with positive attention from the media. A study from the University of North Dakota in 2013 found science fiction in space has been the major influencing factor of interests in space and science (Jackson, 2013). Space scientists almost always answered space entertainment as the gateway to their professional field, such as *Star Trek, Star Wars, Bill Nye the Science Guy,* and *Contact.* The study posits, "Perhaps this is because space-related topics are particularly adept at inspiring imaginations" (Jackson, 2013). In fact, most astrobiologists and astrophysicists I interviewed listed space movies, TV shows, and books as what began their interest in space. The lesson of the story is when we are inspired, we overrule our fear and bravely approach the difficult and daunting, such as the field of space. In a similar vein, if we want to encourage a future generation of space scientists, we must feel inspired even in the face of our fear for aliens.

Dr. Graham Lau, an astrobiologist at the Blue Marble Space Institute of Science (BMSIS), shared what he believes can help us prepare for the coexisting anxiety and excitement of the upcoming new Space Age—meditation. He said, "Meditation is one way to achieve perspective of ourselves," a practice that can be crucial in coming to terms with all the unknown factors when it comes to space. He invited me to a weekly meditation session with a group of people called "The Overwatch Group," where Loretta Hidalgo Whitesides, a Virgin Galactic astronaut and leader in the space exploration community, guided members through a meditation using space as a tool.

It was a transcendent experience. I felt both humbled and transformed as I elevated out of the Earth into outer space, propelled by Whitesides's words, realistic and detailed, no doubt through her own experience as an astronaut. This is commonly coined as the "overview effect," which describes a "cognitive shift in awareness reported by astronauts during space flight, often while viewing the Earth from outer space" (White, 2014). The American Psychological Association conducted an extensive study on the overview effect through astronauts' statements post-flight and affirmed, "Viewing the Earth from space has often prompted astronauts to report overwhelming emotion and feelings of identification with humankind and the planet as a whole" (Yaden, 2016).

Astronaut Edgar Mitchell reported experiencing the overview effect during his two hundred hours in space, including thirty three hours as the sixth person to have walked on the moon. He was also an astronaut in a time of great political turmoil in the 1960s as down on Earth, the world was entangled with the Vietnam War, civil rights protests, the assassination of US President John F Kennedy, and the Cuban Missile Crisis. His quote of his experience in space captures the power of the overview effect with poignancy: "You develop an instant global consciousness, a people orientation, an intense dissatisfaction with the state of the world, and a compulsion to do something about it. From out there on the moon, international politics look so petty. You want to grab a politician by the scruff of the neck and drag him a quarter of a million miles out and say, 'Look at that, you son of a bitch'" (Guarino, 2016).

While we may not all be going to space anytime soon, meditations led by Whitesides attempt to come as close to achieving the overview effect here on Earth. Having gone through the experience myself, I fully agree with Dr. Lau that meditation can keep us grounded and calm our irrational fears. Meditation can help us specifically to separate fact from fiction and turn fear into hope. Our imagination is a formidable tool; it can help us stay hopeful and creative and look forward to potential outcomes with ETI that aren't harmful. Hope is vital in the True Space Age to enter this new era of space exploration in a positive and productive way.

Sadly, perspective may mean we need to separate science fiction from science. We need to remind ourselves what we consume are essentially variations of human stories, while what is really out there cannot be portrayed on paper or on screen.

I'm not going to lie, I'm also afraid. When I think too much about what *could* happen, I easily jump to the worst-case scenarios. I can't help being afraid, but now I understand it is an inseparable instinct in my human nature to brace myself for the worst. Even with the assurance of the scientific community that there is no need to fear, I cannot help reading and watching content on alien invasions. I'm certainly not saying we should cancel *Star Trek* or Marvel films, but paralyzed by our fear, there is no great progress.

It's the small fears that matter—at least for now. Until we do know for sure if there are ETI wishing to interact with us, our powers and responsibility lie in deciphering what is rational and irrational fear. So here is what I tell my brother and what I tell you now: There is importance in recognizing our fear, but an even greater gravity in active hope. To *actively* hope, or to strategize and enact on overcoming our challenges, guarantees we actualize a version of the future we believe in.

Most of us are afraid of the unknown. Astrophobia, fear of space, is similar to thalassophobia, a relatively common fear of the ocean; both are centered on the fear of the unknown. When we imagine swimming in the ocean, far away from the shore without a clue as to what may be swimming below, we feel paralyzed with fear. When we imagine buckling into a spaceship and flying off into space, our mind jumps to scenes from *Gravity* or *The Martian* when errors in spaceships leave at least one astronaut stranded in space, floating aimlessly for all eternity (Cuarón, 2013; Scott, 2015). There is power in the admittance of our fear. Once we admit it, and only when we do, there is an opening for active hope. There will always be the great deep sea we cannot easily navigate and the infinitely vast universe that guilefully conceals its secrets. I encourage you to sit with this unknown and the fear that follows in imagining the unknown, even if only for a moment. Follow the fear as if it were a map showing you where you must dwell and act upon overcoming and the thoughts that are baseless and worth rejecting. On the other side of that journey lies something more beautiful and preciously human—hope.

## CHAPTER 4

# THE TRUE SPACE AGE

I remember the smell of fried chicken and the microwave-size TV as thick as it was wide. The heat of the TV radiated to where I was huddled with my parents and my sister at the short and square-shaped dining table that required us to sit on the floor shoulder to shoulder. This is the greatest memory I have of watching TV as a child. Contrary to the rather ancient technology of the early 2000s, one of the biggest moments of Korean history was unfolding before me on TV—the live reporting of the flight of the first Korean to fly in space, and the astronaut was a *woman.* Her name was Yi So-Yeon (Lutz, 2020). In a truly Korean fashion, our family was celebrating by eating delivery fried chicken and sitting so close to the TV its heat was blasting onto our faces as we ate with our fingers.

On April 8, 2008, Yi launched into space on board Soyuz TMA-12 alongside two Russian astronauts. I remember my family cheering and clapping as the rocket launched, and my heart soared with the spaceship. The next few days, I spent my days filling my sketchbook with drawings of rockets. I had once naively thought spaceships looked like a toy with a triangle attached to a rectangular body with wings on each side. I knew better now. My drawings became 3-D, and I made it skinny and tall with a long spike up top with several fins on its bottom to match the Soyuz TMA-12 spacecraft.

I think everyone goes through a space phase as a child. How can we not? Children only believe what they see. To a child, the limit is the blue sky filled with clouds. The moment they are introduced to the idea there is an entire world beyond the blue sky, a world humans have ventured to, their mind is blown. Their own little Space Age begins from that moment of wonder. For me, my Space Age began at dinner time on April 8, 2008, when a Korean woman, a woman who looked and spoke like me, departed beyond the blue sky on that rocket ship. Without even realizing at the time, the good ol' truism of representation and cultural influence launched me into my own Space Age, making me want to be a part of it and proving I *could* be a part of it. Can you think of a time that spoke to you similarly about space?

I became obsessed with space and tried to understand it within my own capacity. I was just an eight-year-old kid who had barely begun to understand gravity (I had rationalized the goodness of the Earth was keeping us from floating away into the sky), but learning about space became my mission. I decided I must become an astronaut like Yi and fantasized about being in Yi's boots, literally, and dreamt of wearing her astronaut suit and astronaut boots. I told my parents I was going to immigrate to Russia to join their space program.

My Space Age was passionate, but unfortunately short-lived. One night not long after Yi's flight returned to Earth, I sat in a corner of my room, pressed up against the window, looking at the sparkly spots in the night sky and imagining landing my rocket at any one of them. I was thinking of how the stars would compete for my landing spot and pictured how after much anticipation, I would land and leave the rocket, waving in my silver space suit at the space people who long awaited my arrival, when it dawned on me, *Oh no. No, that wouldn't work. I couldn't possibly be an astronaut.* I had eczema as a child, which meant I easily got itchy. I imagined myself in my rocket, about to launch, and an itch would develop inside my elbow or behind my knee, and it would drive me insane. I would jeopardize the whole mission trying to catch the itch. I shook my head sadly at the stars and thought, *So long, space people. I was not meant to be an astronaut.*

Somewhere from then to now, snippets on the news about space caught my eye. I would give it my attention for a few minutes—a new rover landing on a new planet, a new satellite image, scientists' statements of planets that possibly had habitable conditions like Earth—but eventually, I would move on to real-life matters. But something has shifted in the past few years. Space is no longer a snippet on the news, but now it is taking up entire sections, pages, and showing up on my news feed more often than before. What is happening? Am I just gravitating toward space?

It's not just the layperson like me who is noticing increasing stories in the narratives about space. Scientists on the front line of space exploration agree there is a perceptible shift within the space community. Improved technology leads to improved space exploration, and many astrobiologists have noticed the same phenomenon. Dr. Graham Lau of the Blue

Marble Space Institute of Science told me in an interview, "The coming age is going to be the True Space Age." A similar sentiment has been repeated by other astrobiologists that the research in space is dramatically accelerating as technology that assists in space exploration exponentially improves.

One example is the recent evidence presented by an international team of astronomers on the discovery of phosphine in the clouds of Venus in September 2020 (Chang, 2020). Their study added Venus to the list of potentially habitable worlds in our solar system. The only known source of phosphine on Earth is from certain microbes. The presence of phosphine on Venus either means there is a completely unknown method of producing phosphine or there's life on Venus. Goodbye Martians, here come the Venusians! Many scientists shared with me their excitement for this discovery. Dr. Seth Shostak, a famous astrobiologist and planetary scientist, said if proven to be true, "It may be the most interesting discovery on life in space." Dr. Lau, whose fellow researcher at BMSIS was part of the team that made the discovery, has similarly described the potential detection of phosphine in Venus's atmosphere as monumental. He said, "If phosphine is being produced by life, if there currently is life in Venus, life is probably common elsewhere." Dr. Lau describes the buzz in the community as powerful and optimistic.

Another explanation for the buzz is thanks to well-known and wealthy entrepreneurs who are increasingly dedicating their resources to space. Elon Musk, Jeff Bezos, and Richard Branson are all incredibly high-profile figures who have pioneered commercializing spacecraft. Elon Musk founded SpaceX, an aerospace manufacturer and space transportation services company that has worked collaboratively with NASA in launching The SpaceX Dragon, a reusable spacecraft that launched its first manned mission in August 2020. NASA has partnered with Blue Origin (founded by Jeff Bezos) and Dynetics along with SpaceX in the Artemis program, a program whose objective is to send "the first woman and the next man to the Moon by 2024" (Loff, 2019). More ambitiously, NASA and SpaceX are both working separately toward "Moon to Mars"—a goal to send humankind to Mars by 2024 (Mahoney, 2020).

These efforts of private companies shout one thing together: money is entering space. Something else is also clear: humans are also entering space. Over five hundred people have traveled to space so far, yet the buzz is different with the anticipation of Moon to Mars programs. News anticipates the upcoming accomplishments of the "first" woman to land on the moon as well as the return of man on the moon. The same emphasis goes to the "first" human to land on Mars. These accomplishments are dedicated to the human narrative and evoke sentimentality—much like how it was during the Space Race of the 1960s. As the world grew silent on July 16, 1969, for Neil Armstrong to make the first step on the moon and famously say, "That's one small step for man, one giant leap for mankind," incredible moments await the world to go quiet again as history is made. We are dawning an age where space travel histories are being built upon before our eyes.

The year 2024 is approaching fast, and as the first Space Age did in the sixties, this new Space Age enters human history with much anticipation for its advancement in scientific breakthroughs and evolution of technology. Nathan Price is the founder of NSS North Houston Space Society and project

"Countdown to the Moon" (Price, 2021). He has currently interviewed over five hundred people to find out what people think about the future of humanity as we return to the moon and will continue to interview one person a day until the end of 2024, the year NASA plans to land astronauts on the moon. He discovered while most people do not believe we are going to the moon by 2024, support and excitement quickly follows once he informs them of NASA's plan (Price, 2021). Price interviewed Penny, a woman in her sixties who was happily surprised by the information and nostalgic for the excitement from the first moon landing. She said, "I'm one of the generations that actually got to see the first moon landing . . . I've been waiting almost a lifetime to see us go back, so I was super excited to find out about it" (Leinfelder, 2020). Nathan himself is a great example of someone whose profession is outside of space (he works for a software company) but whose belief in the True Space Age is so strong he dedicates extensive amounts of personal time and energy into spreading awareness of space news for other "ordinary" people.

Indeed, we are living in the True Space Age, one that could open a flood of new doors. Multiple existing projects expanded and improved in 2020 to search for intelligent life. In addition to the discovery of phosphine signals in Venus, in 2020, SETI got new receivers for the Allen Telescope Array in Northern California, and both the SETI Institute and the University of California, Berkeley conducted new searches for possible laser technosignatures, indicators of technology developed by advanced civilizations (David, 2019). From expanding the search for alien life from Mars to Venus to SpaceX's successful launching and landing of a fully reusable rocket Spaceship to the ambitious plans underway to send humans to the moon and Mars within the next decade, technological advancements and breakthroughs are growing at a dizzy rate.

However, we are entering the new Space Age with bigger problems left unsolved on Earth. The COVID-19 pandemic inaugurated a wave of calamity and unrest while alienation and active dehumanization wage war online and in person. Biologist David Catling believes we must be wary of discouraging support of outer space exploration because there are problems on Earth. Often he gets asked, "Why do you spend your time working on life on other planets when there are problems here on Earth?" He is confident this is a "false dichotomy because we can also solve problems here as well as solve other problems out there." Most crucially, without interest in outer space, society stagnates because we don't make big discoveries.

When NASA successfully landed its first rocket on the moon, a nun working in Zambia wrote to NASA asking how they could justify spending billions of dollars on the Apollo program when children were starving to death (Siegel, 2018). The letter reached one of the top rocket scientists at NASA, Ernst Stuhlinger, who wrote a lengthy response to the nun, describing how he sees firsthand space advance international cooperation beyond geopolitical tensions, which by extension provides more opportunities for international cooperation on land. He provided the example of Russian ships during the near tragedy of Apollo 13 when the Soviet Union unexpectedly gave the United States support. He believed "had the astronaut capsule touched down near a Russian ship, the Russians would undoubtedly have expended as much care and effort in their rescue as if Russian cosmonauts had returned from a space trip." He added, "If Russian space travelers should ever be in a similar emergency situation, Americans would do the same without any doubt" (Siegel, 2018). Siegel expresses quite eloquently, "Significant progress in the solutions of technical problems is frequently made not by a direct approach, but by first setting a goal of high challenge which offers a strong motivation for innovative work, which fires the imagination and spurs men to expend their best efforts, and which acts as a catalyst by including chains of other reactions" (Siegel, 2018).

pathogens in space

Space exploration has contributed to some of humanity's most vital fields of research for human development, from health care (to prepare for medical issues on spaceflight) to water purification systems (astronauts recycle 93 percent of their water) to natural disaster response (satellites). Particularly relevant in the age of pandemics is the development of improved vaccines through pathogen studies during spaceflight. In 2006, space researchers discovered certain bacteria, in particular Salmonella, could become more pathogenic during spaceflight. Unseen on Earth, key changes in the behavior of genes in the bacteria were unmasked in zero gravity. Disease research is especially critical when conducted in zero gravity space, as it helps researchers get a clearer understanding of their properties, behaviors, and responses to treatments (Dunbar, 2021). Although close to one hundred million cases of Salmonella infections are still reported around the world, space has expedited the process of developing vaccines against the disease (Majowicz, 2010).

Another example that supports Catling and Siegel's point of view is none other than Gen Z's oxygen—the invention of Wi-Fi! Wi-Fi was invented by Australian black hole astronomer

John O'Sullivan who was trying to understand how black holes reduce noise (Kruzelnicki, 2016). While unfortunately, John never found the proof for the noise conundrum, he realized the same mathematics and algorithms of black hole science could be applied to Wi-Fi. In 1992 at the Australian national agency for scientific and industrial research, John tried to invent a reliable and cheap way for "computers to talk to each other without wires" where his black hole mathematics worked like a charm and became the basis of Wi-Fi, the detection of weak, smeared radio signals in a noisy environment (Kruzelnicki, 2016). We can certainly thank astronomy for the most crucial lifeline in the modern century, but it goes beyond just being able to separate problems on Earth to our problems in outer space. I believe we need to learn how to integrate problems on Earth with problems in space.

As we enter the True Space Age, my eight-year-old-self is screaming with joy (Have we figured out a way to make astronauts itch with ease yet?) but my legally adult, twenty-one-year-old self is cautious. Currently, China and the United States both have plans for manned missions to Mars within the next decade, and NASA even invested in a 3-D-printed human habitat design for Mars using Martian dirt (for those curious, it's a cozy, four-floor pod for four habitants with a skylight that looks something between a beehive and an egg) (Wood, 2018). We are hurling into a new era in unfamiliar frontiers, and many questions lie ahead. As with all adventures into the unknown, we need to prepare for what could happen, no matter how small the probabilities may seem. For instance, could these missions accelerate our contact with ETI? What would happen if on these missions, the crew encounters complex, intelligent life? What if our journeys to the moon and Mars in 2024 propel us to be discovered by ETI? These questions are left unanswered by the government and scientists due to the low probability that it could happen. The answers to these questions are often a startling return to the problems on Earth—of alienation, of institutional functionality, and of empathy.

A better method for preparing for the Space Age will be to work collaboratively with our problems on Earth that can project onto outer space. Without progress in our collaboration here on Earth, any achievements in space exploration will remain restricted to a segment of our humanity—false and alienating progress. As Abhijit Naskar, a world-famous neuroscientist and advocate of global peace, states, "True progress means progress of all humans from all walks of life, not just the progress in science or progress in technology" (Naskar, 2015).

# PART 2

# TOUCH DOWN

## CHAPTER 5

# PRINCIPLES OF ENGAGEMENT: EMPATHY, PURPOSE, AND PATIENCE

"Everything that has ever been written or made about aliens has been about us and only us."

That's what anthropologist Kathryn Denning said as we discussed the books and movies that decorated the hall of fame in science fiction. When she first agreed to the interview, I was eager to ask her about her research at the intersection of anthropology and the search for extraterrestrial intelligence. I came prepared with questions such as "From your study of humanity, how do you predict we will respond to the scenario when we are discovered by or when we discover ETI?" and "How can we prepare for the least amount of chaos and uncertainty?" I was disappointed when she said she couldn't answer any of my questions. As we talked, the reason quickly revealed itself. The problem was my assumption of a "we."

In my mind, the "we" represented all of us—all of humanity. It seemed a given premise when I began writing this book because in the question of ETI, there is only one clear distinction between the aliens and us—which is we are one singular species and the aliens another. This premise is commonly given in most science fiction novels and movies as well. The humans are one singular identity united against the enemies from the outer space. Denning pointed out the obvious: we are, and will forever be, a diverse species of different cultures and tongues. She made me question why I believed the premise that humanity will be united was true as she asked, "Us? Who is us?" She was right. As she put it, "A unified humanity is not how we deal with things. It's not them versus Earth because one of our key characteristics as humans is our diversity."

Faced with a united threat against humanity, such as malevolent ETI, experts do not believe we will be united. Instead, scientists predict some people, groups, or countries will be quick to try to betray each other for selfish purposes. In our conversation in 2020, Senior Astronomer at SETI, Dr. Seth Shostak, listed North Korea's authoritarian leader Kim Jong Un as one such unknown variable. He warned, "Nothing will stop people like Kim Jong Un from establishing a separate communication channel between the ETI and North Korea, especially if the technology is available, such as radio signals." He believed given the means, people will be quick to try to act for their own gain, even if it was shortsighted.

There is no law or international institution that guarantees a coalition of countries even when faced with a question that applies to all of humanity. Without a legal regime and enforcement, there is not much chance of a unified, coordinated, diplomatic effort. Denning added that cultural differences pose a barrier. She explained, "Due to cultural and communication differences on Earth, the Earth cannot hold a united front against ETI."

But let's return for a second to what Denning has said about fictional content on aliens and humans. Everything that has ever been written or made about aliens has been about us and only us. Denning believes our popular culture on aliens is about us in every detail: "It's about Earthly others, the tensions, those we fear, those with whom we engage positively . . . It's really about us."

So my question is, If we are not united in real life, why do popular movies on alien invasions depict us as a single, united species?

This is the answer I present: we wish we were more united. Despite our conflict, we understand on some level we would be better off working together, and that's the key to moving forward. Yes, this time I do intend to use "we" to represent all of humanity. If the movies and TV shows reflect our truest hopes, fears, and tensions, then the international success of this content shows that despite our disunity in real life, at the end of the day, we want to be more strongly united. The common threat against humanity, such as aliens invading Earth, provides us a simple escape to a utopian future where we are no longer alienated from one another. We believe in this future because we crave it.

What's more interesting to me is even those aliens invading Earth—the common threat uniting all humans—are, in actuality, ourselves. Remember, everything that has ever been written or made about aliens has been about us and only us. The aliens, as Denning puts it, are our "Earthly others." The aliens we imagine simply reflect our own fears, expectations, and struggles, often in forms of human "others" like different groups, cultures, and countries. The dangers we fear do not come from outer space, but from right here on Earth.

So here is a dilemma. Are we capable of being united against a common threat if that threat is ourselves? It's a catch-22, a circumstance from which there is no escape because of mutually conflicting conditions. To fight off the aliens, it seems we must fight ourselves. But when I unravel this paradox, an answer seems apparent: we need to stop treating and thinking of each other as aliens. To truly be united, we need to stop alienating each other.

We all have aliens in our own lives. We are afraid of them without a logical reason, and we have been afraid of them for as long as we can remember. We don't remember the exact moment they became our enemies because they were *always* there, waiting for the opportunity to take away our livelihoods or steal our jobs, according to our uninformed grandparents. They threaten our loved ones, our country, and the values we live for. They are evil-minded and represent everything we stand against. Did something or someone come up in your mind as I described these aliens? They are on the TV screen, green, slippery, slimy creatures that fly on space disks. Beneath these masks, they are our own neighbors, our classmates, living across our countries' borders or across the ocean, yet all on this planet.

We have always fixated on an "other"—indigenous people and the colonists, the Soviet Union and the United States, Mexico and United States, Korea and Japan, Denmark and Sweden. We are our own aliens, which is why what we read and watch on space will only be as real of a threat as how we perceive our own aliens. Conflict with aliens resembles racial, political, and cultural relations right here in our own lives.

In our imagination, the extraterrestrial aliens become the "bad guys" and us the "good guys," and the bad and good is simple and clear-cut, as we often perceive the "aliens" in our own lives to be. This reduction of a more complicated reality to the good and bad is largely facilitated by negative stereotypes and prejudices we associate with those we consider as "other." One example of such an imagination that became a worldwide pop-culture phenomenon is *Star Wars.* While the movie's alienation of certain cultures and peoples is subtle, it is copious. Jeffrey C. J. Chen, a PhD student in history at Stanford University and the co-host of *The Global History Podcast* writes that *Star Wars* is shot with "Orientalizing" stereotypes—patronizing tropes that represent an imagined East, or the Orient, as inferior to the rational, heroic West (Chen, 2019).

He explains the plot is thick with "the uniformed conformity of the evil Empire versus the scrappy (American) individualism of the rebel heroes, the vague Eastern mysticism of the Force, and its Shaolin-cum-Samurai practitioners, and the uncomfortable racial stereotypes embodied in the hookah-smoking Jabba and the miserly Watto" (Chen, 2019). Chen notes even the famous music by John Williams plays a role as the "good guys" such as Luke, Leia, and Rey are associated with the grand orchestral style of the European Romantics while the themes for the "bad guys" are expressed in the vocabulary of Chinese, Indian, and Middle Eastern music. Stereotypes a Western audience might easily associate with the "others" in real life are utilized on screen to perpetuate prejudices.

Is the extent of our imagination regarding space and ETI bound to our own prejudices and conflict on Earth? Unfortunately, this has rung true when it comes to so many successful Hollywood movies such as *Star Wars*, *Star Trek*, and *Avatar*. But we should not be discouraged by Hollywood narratives from facing and deconstructing alienation in our own lives. While movies are powerful, their storytelling is meant for inspiration, not deterrence. If anything, we can be motivated by the limitations on screen to test our minds further and actualize a greater future, a future that embraces diversity rather than weaponizing it.

We need the right principles for engaging with our "aliens" on Earth—each other. Guided by the right set of beliefs, we can have positive engagement with fictional aliens and actual aliens, or at least the "aliens" we are so often afraid of in our minds. The principles are guided by each of our potentials; in this way, the responsibility for us to paint a better future with regards to Earth and space is returned to ourselves rather than "up to the unknown."

First, we each need to prioritize exercising cognitive empathy where natural, emotional empathy is lacking. Scientists claim there are intricate ties between "evolutionary biases" and empathy, especially among people with visible or cultural differences. One 2017 Harvard Medical School Empathy and Relational Science Program study claims, "Individuals tend to have the most empathy for others who look or act like them, for others who have suffered in a similar way, or for those who share a common goal" (Reiss, 2017). Therefore, human species are evolutionarily wired to only feel emotional empathy among members of the same "tribe." According to this science, due to the evolutionary bias, cognitive empathy—actively exercising the capacity to see a person's situation from their point of view—must play a role when a lack of emotional empathy exists because of racial, ethnic, religious, or physical differences (Reiss, 2017). Studies show bias can be successfully overridden with cognitive empathy, proving the power of empathy (Reiss, 2017).

Often, we dehumanize and alienate another human being because of our differences, but difference does not make us unequal. The most powerful path to turn your enemy into your friend is to use our uniquely human ability to put yourself in their position and understand who they are and what they are feeling. We possess the unique ability to do so as humans. Cognitive empathy, more than our innate emotional empathy, is perhaps our most formidable ability as a species. It teaches us to truly understand the human experience beyond our own experience when we aren't easily able to. It allows us to live a bigger world and understand our differences, even our enemies.

I'm in a unique position to talk about enemies because I was born and live in a country still at war. Only twenty-three kilometers north of my home in Seoul, there is the land of South Korea's "enemy," North Korea. As a civilian, I'd never encountered a North Korean and only heard of them through the news and learned about them from textbooks. In these sources, North Korea was always depicted as a force of cruelty and uncertainty that could not be accounted for. After all, if we all decided to befriend our enemy, there would be no war.

I understood not all North Koreans were enemies, given they were mostly the notorious Kim family and their tyrannical regime. But in all honesty, my interest never extended to the twenty-five million ordinary North Koreans living in the shadows whose voices are strictly silenced by the regime. In moments, I pitied the anonymous North Korean civilians for their suffering and poverty. What I never fully grasped was North Koreans are people who look like me and speak like me and who South Koreans shared a history and culture with for thousands of years before its forced separation only fifty years ago. Information about our shared history was never enough to help me humanize the people up north; empathy was crucial to understanding the North Koreans. My first opportunity came when I first met my North Korean peer on the first floor of a dorm at Georgetown University.

On a school night early in my first semester in college, there was a play organized and performed by a dozen North Korean defectors in a small hall of the dormitory. They were a humanitarian organization that, through their amateur acting, traveled the world to raise awareness about the malnutrition, starvation, abuse, and various other human rights violations against North Korean citizens. The skit contained scenes that mirrored their own starvation, abuse from the government, and life-and-death efforts to defect. After the passionate and tearful play, I approached one of the actors who seemed as young, or younger, than me called Young-Mi but was at a loss for words. I couldn't believe I'd met a North Korean halfway across the world when I lived only an hour away from her country back home.

I introduced myself in English and quickly changed to Korean as I realized my silliness; we both spoke the same language. The truth behind my stuttering was that I was stunned. I was stunned it took an impulsive decision to watch a play on a school night lured by the organization's advertisement for free Korean food for me to finally realize my lack of empathy for the North Korean people. I had almost skipped the play, preoccupied with my midterm studies. Their play jolted me awake from my ignorance and antagonization of the North, and I was forced to realize the undeniable similarity between Young-Mi and me. Only, on this September night, my biggest priority was my school assignment, while for Young-Mi, in the past ten years, their biggest priority was survival.

After that night, I joined Truth and Human Rights in North Korea, an organization dedicated to humanitarian aid and awareness of North Korean citizens and dropped most of my other commitments. Instilling empathy for North Koreans for those unaware—even in South Korean students who lived nearby like me—became one of the most important goals in my college years.

As I experienced, empathy helps us remember at the end of the day, the enemies' or aliens' larger labels—North Koreans, illegal immigrants, Americans, Mexicans, Chinese—are not the individuals themselves. Given the chance to understand who they are, we realize we have much more in common than we believed. They do not need to share an ancestor with you nor speak the same language nor even look like you. When faced with a bigger threat, we may just realize the most important thing we have in common with each other is our humanity.

The second principle for positive engagement with "aliens" is to maintain a common purpose. This principle applies most strongly to institutional cooperation. There can rarely be positive engagement without understanding a common long-term goal among large groups of people. It is easy to generalize harmful stereotypes to one another when we fail to understand where we come from and where we are headed. As is argued by institutional neoliberalism, a principal theory in international relations, international institutions can allow nations to successfully cooperate in the international system and reduce war while prolonging peaceful cooperation.

Immanuel Kant, one of the founders of liberalism, voiced the importance of economic interdependence and free trade as keys to perpetual peace in his essay "To Perpetual Peace" (Kant, 1903). One clear example of cooperation through common purpose I can draw from the East Asian region is how the Japanese, Chinese, and Korean governments were able to form close relations through trade partnerships and other economic interdependence despite their recent years of war and conflict. Relations between people are significantly more positive when nations are cooperating on an institutional level.

On an individual level, we need to remember the common purposes that tie us together: to protect our family, ensure a brighter future for our children, to conserve our environment, and to preserve our freedom, among other goals. On a more institutional level, the purpose can be for economic development or preventing war. All common purposes are pragmatic solutions to overcoming our fear of "others" on all levels.

Lastly, we need to remember patience, or more precisely, patience to fight our cognitive and systemic biases. It is a difficult process to unlearn what we were taught to distrust, dehumanize, and alienate. One example is racism—a particularly divisive belief commonly taught to us from a young age and the root cause of much alienation and dehumanization. Studies say children pick up biases, especially racism, quicker than we expect, as young as the age of three.

One 2011 study by Mahzarin Banaji, a Harvard University psychologist, states, "Children exposed to racism tend to accept and embrace it as young as age three, and in just a matter of days" (James, 2012). While we pick up biases such as racism quickly, it takes a much longer time for us to unlearn biases. Without patience, we don't stand a chance to free ourselves from prejudices preventing us from connecting to a bigger world. Andrew, my classmate from my Middle East US Foreign Policy class, is one clear example. He learned of his bias against people he was taught to alienate and dehumanize with defensiveness at first, then with painstaking awareness, which he then attempted to unlearn throughout the course of the semester. We can always learn to think and live differently, no matter how different we may see other people.

I was taught by my parents and Korean society at large to dehumanize and alienate a lot of people in the world. The list was long: the Japanese, the Chinese, as well as the North Korean regime. They all came with their string of justified reasons and historical context. For a while, it seemed the world was black and white between the "good" people and the "bad." But slowly, I'm discovering a more complex and colorful world. As Denning reminded me, "One of our key characteristics as humans is our diversity." Diversity, while often exploited as a weapon, a time-old starting point of human conflict, is also the greatest tool for unity.

Diversity drives empathy, purpose, and patience. With empathy, I've made new friends from worlds I considered "alien" as well as gratitude for the world I come from. With purpose, I understand the significance of diplomacy, peaceful international relations, and cooperation and progress from an individual to an institutional level. Our prejudices can be more easily fought paired with a top-down effort. With patience, I am hopeful for my own progress as well as the rest of the world's, one person at a time.

My grandparents were born during the Japanese occupation of Korea in the 1930s and lived to see the end of the Korean War in 1953. They saw atrocities I cannot begin to imagine, even as they speak of the war as if it happened yesterday. They passed their fears and traumas to my parents, and in turn, my parents instilled the same precaution in me. For them, aliens are much more real. They are more susceptible to narratives in space operas that reflect Earthly political conflict in a form of alien invasion because they understand the fear of the "other" very personally.

Yet time has been kind to me, as I have lived in a period different to theirs, albeit short and inexperienced, but rich with opportunities to understand my fear of aliens on Earth and in space and actualize my hopes to coexist with them. With this privilege, I hope to raise awareness of the responsibility in each of us to ensure there are no more "aliens" on our planet. I hope to present all of us with the tools that can help in that difficult fight toward such a future.

When asked about aliens in a 2021 *New York Times Podcast*, President Obama spoke about our ability to find common ground if aliens were revealed to be real. He said, "I would hope that the knowledge that there were aliens out there would solidify people's sense that what we have in common is a little more important" (Klein, 2021). I watched many news sources report his claim in an optimistic light, with news speaking about President Obama's faith in our ability to "unite." Yet, in the full podcast, I found what he said immediately after more important to note: "But no doubt, there would be immediate arguments . . . We're good at manufacturing arguments for each other." Indeed, our biases are real and so are inclinations to be in conflict.

As we search for aliens out in space, we must take a hard look at ourselves. While "we" are people of all different backgrounds, juxtaposed with extraterrestrial life, *there is a "we."* No matter who you are, you and I both have a claim to humanity. Our humanity may not be on the forefront of our minds in day-to-day life but put in the context of the upcoming plans to make humanity a multi-planetary species in the True Space Age and suddenly, the one undeniable thing we have in common is underscored. It's an interesting mind-set where we must both be hyperaware of what we have in common and, simultaneously, what we don't have in common. But this is exactly what we need to tackle our false "aliens" here on Earth.

We're exploring, we're waiting, and we're seeking every day for signs that we are not alone beyond the exosphere. Look around and you can engage with someone you considered to be so different from you, an alien of our own making, right here in our atmosphere. I assure you the kind of alien engagement you envision need not be far off. We have a great opportunity to enhance our principles and actions of positive engagement with those we don't relate to right here on Earth. Our diversity, the one common factor paradoxically dividing us and uniting us, is our greatest blessing in disguise. As Obama said, "The differences we have on this planet are real, they're profound, and they cause tragedy as well as joy . . . The best thing we can do is treat each other better because we're all we got" (Klein, 2021).

Until proven otherwise, *we're all we got*, and everything that has ever been written or made about aliens has been about us and only us. While the aliens reflect our truest fears and hopes, so do the heroes in every story. We live in a time where we are desperate for role models, heroes, and stories of unity and triumph. Without empathy, purpose, or patience, we risk seeking the wrong role models and alienating innocent people. How much are we learning and internalizing from the storytelling about alien invasions and space colonization without thinking twice about it? We think of these stereotypes as purely fictional, but we're still absorbing the political messages that could shape the way we think in our day-to-day lives as well as years into the future.

Though "alien" we may be to each other, you and I are entering the True Space Age together. For the remainder of our journey, I hope you remember we are stronger because of our differences and our humanity. I ask you to join me in holding on to these basic principles—empathy, purpose, and patience—as we further explore how to positively engage with aliens of all kinds both here on Earth and in outer space in the True Space Age.

CHAPTER 6

# PRINCIPLES OF ENGAGEMENT: COMMUNICATION

I bought five tickets for my family to watch *Avengers: Endgame* (Russo, 2019). As I had promised my parents, I booked the tickets weeks in advance, ensuring we had the optimal seats in the optimal room (two-thirds of the way back instead of dead center in AMC Dolby Cinema is the golden ratio). #NerdandProud.

Excitement was an understatement for my younger brother, who had blocked his ears and screamed each time anyone mentioned something remotely related to *Endgame* for the past month. I felt for him since I also hate spoilers. The anticipation was building each day.

When I finally sat down in that theater to watch what we knew would become the highest-grossing movie of all time (and indeed it did), my heart raced (Welle, 2019). I impatiently waited for the movie to begin, to be swept away by the action and plot twists that would keep me on the edge of my seat until the closing credits. To my left was my brother, who looked almost meditative as he concentrated on the blank screen in front of him. To my right was a Mandarin-speaking couple who whispered to each other in bubbly anticipation. I smiled, feeling like I was sandwiched in the optimal community full of Marvel fans like me. I felt a sense of camaraderie with these strangers.

Once *Endgame* began with the iconic theme song, I was sucked into the world of *Avengers* (Russo, 2019). Marvel heroes fought in immaculately choreographed fight scenes. The computer graphics blurred the line between reality and possibility with ease. The story line was immaculate and gripping. Then came the emotional climax—and as it intended, my heart stopped. Black Widow dived off the cliff for Hawkeye to retrieve the Soul Stone. The thud that followed her jump took my breath away, and audible gasps echoed throughout the theater.

I denied the possibility she was dead for good. Black Widow was one of my favorite characters, and I couldn't imagine a core member of *Avengers* was truly gone. I exhaled and thought, *Perhaps there is another epic plot twist coming.*

That's when I clearly heard:

"Ta zhen de si le ma? Zhen de?"

"Deng yi xia . . . Dui, dui, dui, ta zhen de si le."

The couple next to me whisper-shouted at each other. Translated literally, the woman asked, "Did she really die? For real?" to which the boyfriend whispered back, "Wait a second" and pulled out his phone to quickly search and confirm, "Yes, yes, yes. She really died."

*Oh my god?* I screamed internally. The couple had ruined my hope. Even worse, throughout the rest of the movie, the woman repeatedly asked her boyfriend if a certain character was "zhen de si le?" or "dead for real," to which the man would diligently pull out his phone and deny or confirm. What a good boyfriend he was. I wasn't sure if I should laugh or cry. Here's a summary of my experience in that theater: Black Widow died twice for me, and so did Iron Man.

Iron Man was the last straw. I finally asked him in Mandarin to kindly put away the phone, but the harm was done.

The one silver lining in this experience was out of all my family members, I was the only one who understood Mandarin. My brother was blissfully unaware of what had ruined my experience. If the couple had spoken English, Spanish, or Korean and had sat next to my brother instead of me, I can imagine the experience would have ended in a pool of a fifteen-year-old's tears.

Still, I left the theater fuming, and in a moment of uncontrollable disappointment, I wished I had never learned Mandarin.

That was the first and only time I have ever regretted learning a language because the truth is being multilingual is endlessly giving. I have plenty more examples where my intermediate Mandarin saved me an embarrassing moment when I was traveling, helped me make lifelong friends, and broadened my world. Every language I have ever learned—English, Vietnamese, French, Danish, and Mandarin—have introduced me to people, cultures, and perspectives I could not have approached otherwise.

I'm not alone in my experience. Around the world, more than half of all people—estimates vary from 60–75 percent—speak at least two languages (Vince, 2016). To be monolingual is to be in the minority, as many people enjoy the social, psychological, and lifestyle advantages of multilingualism (Vince, 2016).

While spoken languages are the most common form of communication, communication between two people can expand even beyond verbal methods.

If I didn't speak Mandarin, would I have been able to ask the Mandarin-speaking couple to stop spoiling *Endgame*? It's likely, since we watched the movie in Boston, I could have asked them in English and they would have understood. Even if we didn't share a common language, I could have used body language, pointing to his phone and shaking my head. Or he could have just read my facial expression, which possibly looked murderous, and gotten the hint.

Among humans, it's hard for communication to fail. As we rely on a few sensory tools to describe our purposes—auditory, visual, kinesthetic, olfactory—there is guaranteed to be some combination of our existing communication tools we can use to relay what we mean.

But how would communication work when we confront a life-form that doesn't share any of our senses? There is no guarantee something that enters our atmosphere will have evolved with the same sensory factors in its body. What guarantees they have eyes, ears, or skin? What guarantees they even have bodies? What if they are gaseous creatures who float around in amorphous forms?

These are the kinds of questions we need answers to before we can begin to attempt communication with aliens. If we were to discuss all possible scenarios, this book will be thicker and more multi-volumed than your grandfather's *Encyclopedia Britannica*. But I'm determined to show you this is still a question worth pondering. Even if we don't have the answers to extraterrestrial intelligence communication anytime soon, it's a great mind exercise that will instill a deep appreciation for languages on Earth. Unfolding how we will communicate with aliens will teach us language comes in many forms, expressing the diversity of humankind's ability to communicate. Language is the core of all communities and is essential in manifesting and connecting communities. In today's world, as statistics above show, we are inclined to try; we should go beyond bilingualism and strive to be multilingual.

First, let's think of a scenario. Enter, Planet B.

In our scenario, Planet B is equidistant from us on the opposite side in our orbit to the sun with a similar mass and size of Earth and equal exposure to sunlight. Planet B is a habitable planet, and on it evolved a multitude of living species. Against all odds, there evolved one complex, sentient, intelligent species that would reach the apex of the food chain. For whatever reason (e.g., massive scientific blunder, ignorance, Area 51, magical fairy dust, whatever helps) let's imagine Earth and Planet B never knew of each other's existence—until one day. Admittedly, this scenario would open a Pandora's box of existential questions, but for the sake of simplicity and keeping things to the point, the question to consider is, How would we communicate with them?

Planet B is essentially an extreme project for field linguists who are learning an entirely new language of a group of people they are completely unfamiliar with.

Oh, there's something I forgot to mention about Planet B: its most intelligent beings, or its "people" to our planet, don't speak. They don't communicate using any auditory, visual, kinesthetic, or olfactory tools. In fact, they aren't corporeal beings! They exist on the "cloud," and their minds are synced up to technological devices that output their thoughts efficiently. To them, our Facebook messages are analog. Our concept of communication is a vintage bygone. They share jokes in the fifth dimension, and we can't even share a laugh. Obviously, I'm spurting a load of bullshit, but you get my point. They are unicorns, and we wouldn't even know where to begin to learn how to communicate with them. Is it pointless to try to communicate with beings we don't understand? Should we try, knowing we can't?

The answer is yes because communication is the bridge to connection with an "other." No matter how difficult the process and how long it takes to establish an equal mode of communication, we will fail at any attempt of diplomacy and peaceful coexistence without it. This returns to the ideas of "others" on Earth and how we easily alienate and dehumanize people (or even animals) we don't understand because we don't share the same culture or language.

The "aliens" on Planet B are what linguists would consider radical versions of "uncontacted communities" here on Earth. If we rewind the dial to a few hundred years ago, plenty of historical examples abound of what ensued when those communities were contacted.

One example of first interactions where people were learning of "alien languages" on Earth is when the Portuguese missionaries first landed in Japan in the 1500s (Kono, 2001). This period is also aptly known as "Contact Period," defined as the time in which seafaring European nations explored regions across the globe (Encyclopædia, 2021). Sure, the Japanese were already trading with the Chinese, Koreans, and "others" in the island's vicinity, but the Japanese and the Portuguese were aliens to each other. The clash between the two cultures was dramatic.

To the Japanese, the Portuguese were the first Europeans to step on their land (Kono, 2001). The Portuguese seemed like animals who used fingers to eat instead of chopsticks and worshiped a strange god. To the Portuguese, the Japanese were pitifully isolated islanders who seemed a tiny vassal to the Chinese, desperately in need of a salvaging religion. Shady first impressions were written by notetakers who reflected their weirded-out feelings of the other's differences and reassured the superiority of their own country (Lidin, 2004). In other words, alienation and dehumanization manifested in all their glory. Japan's rejection of these strange visitors and their influences, especially the Europeans, was so strong that Japan eventually kicked them all out and banned foreigners from entering for more than two hundred years (Lidin, 2004).

Language-wise, the Portuguese's influence would stick. Today, some of Japan's modern vocabulary has strong ties to the Portuguese language, including its word for velvet and deep-fried vegetables and fish. We can thank the Portuguese for our beloved tempura platters on the side of our sushi. The Portuguese were not only the conveyor of the delicious term "tempura" but they were also the ones who introduced the deep-frying technique to the Japanese (Farley, 2017). Language was a crucial bridge between the two cultures and the starting point of all relations between the two nationalities.

The Portuguese missionaries acted as field linguists, creating the first Western dictionary for the Japanese language, the *Nippo Jisho*, by deciphering with nuances, body language, and context (Morita, 1961). The Japanese language is a footprint of the cultural exchange and (yummy) fruits of collaboration between the Japanese and the Portuguese. However, most of their relations were long periods of interstate hostility. If Planet B interactions were to go down exactly as it did between Japan and the Europeans, there would no doubt be a lot of conflict for most relations—resistance from religious conversion, slavery, and world wars. Miraculously, once the communication succeeds and diplomacy blooms, there would be momentary periods of peace.

The Portuguese missionaries were deeply aware of the language barrier, a barrier that seemed insurmountable given the Japanese were a community entirely alien to them with no prior textbooks nor references to help them. Studies suggest the Portuguese missionaries took at least six years before "one could hear confession in Japanese and fifteen [years] before one could preach to the Christians" (Vande, 1996). One missionary wrote in a letter back home, "However much we learn of the language and with however much effort, we still sound like children compared to them" (Vande, 1996). Despite the incredible challenge, the missionaries were keenly aware of the need to master the Japanese language if the mission were ever to succeed, and they persevered for decades, opening the gates to future Japanese-European relations. They understood the importance of successful communication, especially through learning each other's languages, to establish a true human-to-human connection.

Interestingly, the first moment of a language barrier breakthrough is recorded as a theological dispute between a missionary and Japanese monk (Vande, 1996). It's important to note a deep, ideological conflict represented a successful human-to-human interaction between the two groups, and it makes sense. Ideological conflict absent of violence but full of ideas and words represents mutual respect and understanding on a fundamental and human level. We can certainly learn from their example and apply the lesson to scenarios with real aliens. To move beyond distrust and assumptions of war and violence, we must be able to communicate with respect and fundamental understanding of each other's ideologies. It's easy to assume the other's best or worst intentions when we cannot understand their beliefs.

So perhaps instead of asking if there is a way to ensure we can avoid conflicts in our communication with Planet B, perhaps we should accept conflict is an inevitable part of the process. The Portuguese and the Japanese show us the role of language in establishing relations between them is the bridge to peaceful relations. Quite appropriately in theme with our topic, their relationship is often cited as the exemplary interaction between two "alien" cultures in the "Age of Discovery," another name for "Contact Period" (Encyclopædia, 2021).

There is something to be said about communications failing even when we do have the same system of language.

Earlier I said, "Among humans, it's hard for communication to fail." Well, here's more accurately what I was trying to say: Among humans, it's hard for communication to fail, *but it does, every single day.* I can't relay to my own mother exactly why it frustrates me that she keeps forgetting my seafood allergies. I go to my professors hoping to ask them for an extension on a few assignments and come out of their office having *volunteered* to submit two new assignments. I tell someone I like exactly how much he annoys me, hoping my second-grade reverse psychology works on him. We're all speaking the same language, we possess the same communication tools, yet none of our messages get across. Hopefully you're not as epically bad as I am in my everyday life.

It's moments like my failed attempts to express honesty or flirt that evoke immense frustration and curiosity at the wonder that the human race has survived for this long while being this bad at communication. When confronted with the question of how we would communicate with species who don't share a common language, similar language tools, or even the same definition of "communication," my head explodes.

One thing is clear. I'm grateful for the simplicity of the human language and simultaneously astonished by the difficulty and complexity of our communication. We need to appreciate the richness and complexity of our communication and the backbone of our communication: languages, all *seven thousand* of them, according to Ethnologue (Ethnologue, 2021). We cannot take for granted the languages we have opportunities to learn. Languages provide the easiest and most important tool of engaging peacefully with an "other" on Earth. To communicate is to build a relationship. If we are to become a more united species, humanity needs to make a better effort to become a multilingual, multicultural species, interconnected despite our various tongues and cultures and united in our universal truth that is diversity.

If "just because we can" is not a good enough answer for you to appreciate "language" as a concept, spread your multilingual wings and devote more hours to learning that language the Duolingo owl reminds you about with a chilling message ("Hi, it's Duo! Looks like you forgot your Spanish lesson again. You Know What Happens Now!").

For the intensely practical audience, there are great cognitive benefits of learning a new language. Speaking a second language has been proven by several studies to prevent Alzheimer's and dementia by improving your memory (Reporters, 2018). It also helps you make more rational decisions according to a study from the University of Chicago (Keysar, 2012). If you are too busy trying to wrap your head around your first language, don't worry, learning another language can help you as well. A second language education improves your native language by helping you become more aware of the mechanics of language (Keysar, 2012). Languages exist to serve everyone.

But most importantly, language introduces you to a new culture, a new perspective, and a new way of life, which helps you become more empathetic and just a more decent person. Several studies have stated multilinguals are more understanding and able to show empathy, which is rooted in their learned skills to be perceptive and flexible (Fan, 2015). As a bilingual (trilingual when I'm feeling extra pretty) person myself, I'm not biased at all. *Obviously*, I'm great at thinking in other people's shoes. I think I do overdo it sometimes, and it *may* be a problem. I am writing a book centered on viewing it from the alien's perspective, after all.

But I am a firm believer language is more than just the mechanics, the grammar, and its intonations. Behind every language is a unique culture, community, and history. I often imagine it's another "planet" I'm entering when I study a new language. Plus, I'm always pleasantly surprised by how similar languages can be. For instance, every language I've learned has a word for "mom" that begins with an "m," while most words for fathers include a "ph—" or "p" sound. The explanation experts provide is because the words for "mom" and "dad" are often based on the sounds babies can make the easiest (McWhorter, 2015). Just babbling to themselves, babies' first words are often something like mama, papa, baba, nana, dada, etc. Learning new languages reminds me some things in the human experience are uncontrollably universal.

Sadly, we don't celebrate the diversity of languages enough. While the majority of countries study English as a second language, most primarily English-speaking countries don't care for advocating multilingualism in their education. For instance, while most countries in Europe sustain rigorous foreign language education policies, almost every country's most studied foreign language is English (Devlin, 2021). Administrative decisions in both lower and higher education in the United States reflect a lack of appreciation and a serious disregard of the value of fostering curiosity toward language learning in students. In 2019, the Modern Language Association made an astonishing announcement that from 2013 to 2016, colleges across the United States cut 651 foreign language programs. This alone is a ghastly showcase of the entitlement of English-speaking cultures and displays how they neglect linguistic diversity (Johnson, 2020). The situation is not much better in Asia. Most countries in Southeast Asia and East Asia concentrate their foreign language education on English or Mandarin (Kobayashi, 2013). Exposure to diversity in languages is hard to find in both early and later education across the world.

The supremacy of English, and in some cases Mandarin, equals the death of multilingualism. One study has shown the rise of English as an international language has caused "critical concerns about the future of languages other than English" (Kobayashi, 2013). This is an alarming phenomenon because communication is the one lifeline to understanding one other on a deeper level and is a critical tool in battling dehumanization and alienation.

Meanwhile, linguist Thomas Edward Payne predicts "3,000 of the 6,000 or so natural human languages now spoken will become extinct during the present century, unless some positive action is taken" (Payne, 1997). Payne warns the loss of diversity that language extinction represents is a scientific and human tragedy. When a language dies, "All potential for enriching human experience embodied in the oral tradition and wisdom of that culture is lost forever" (Payne, 1997). Not only is there a danger of a few languages becoming the select few that the human society amalgamates but there are also dangers of languages being lost, and along with it, their cultures becoming extinct.

There is a journey of self-improvement in learning languages. I'm proud to be able to write a book today in English when my eight-year-old self could barely finish the English alphabet. While it is important to learn languages to be smarter and cooler, what is overlooked and cannot be simply proven by studies and statistics is that there is beauty and something so deeply *human* in learning languages. Language is a celebration of humanity's ability to connect, collaborate, and communicate.

So, you can suck it, Planet B, and your 9999999G telecommunication system. Please stay nonexistent forever, or at least don a slightly cooler name.

At this point Planet B may be sounding a little familiar to you. Indeed, I derived it from its famous usage as the "alternate

Earth." Al Gore, former vice president of the United States and environmentalist tweeted on Earth Day of 2019, "What we should remember today and every day: We share Mother Earth as our only home. *There is no Planet B*" (Gore, 2019). Former United Nations Secretary-General Ban Ki-Moon also spoke of Planet B at a speech in 2013, "There can be no Plan B because there is no Planet B," as he listed sustainable development as one of the United Nations's highest priorities (Ban, 2013). Planet B is a powerful evocation by environmentalists who wish to remind everyone of the value of Earth; and I agree, Planet B does not, and cannot, exist if we truly value Earth.

It's a dangerous exercise to think of what Planet B would look like because we begin to overlook what we can work on here on Earth. But consciously evoking Planet B could also help us better understand the value of Earth. It's crazy how something completely hypothetical and extraterrestrial can teach us gratitude and appreciation for the simple things in life. Language is one.

CHAPTER 7

# PRINCIPLES OF ENGAGEMENT: SOFT POWER AND CULTURAL DIPLOMACY

*"Voyager did things no one predicted, found scenes no one expected, and promises to outlive its inventors . . . Like a great painting or an abiding institution, it has acquired an existence of its own, a destiny beyond the grasp of its handlers."*

—ENVIRONMENTAL HISTORIAN STEPHEN J. PYNE.

Every second as you read, two NASA *Voyager* spacecrafts are setting new records for traveling the furthest distance from Earth. Launched in 1977, the spacecrafts had no specific destination in mind. They were simply allowed to explore the deepest crevices of space, and they did. On August 25, 2012, NASA announced *Voyager 1* became the first man-made object to enter interstellar space, "traveling further than anyone, or anything, in history" (NASA, 2013). On November 5, 2019, NASA announced *Voyager 2* had also entered interstellar space. *Voyager 2* joined its sister spacecraft, *Voyager 1*, in the "interstellar medium," a region of outer space outside of our own solar system (Greicius, 2013). Today, the spacecrafts wander separately in one cosmos, planned to pass within 1.6 light-years' distance to a star in the constellation Camelopardalis in about forty thousand years (Greicius, 2013).

The spacecrafts' objectives have been successfully executed thus far: to explore space carrying our message. Both spacecrafts carry a twelve-inch (30 cm) golden phonograph record called "The Golden Record" containing pictures and sounds of Earth, directions on the cover for playing the record, and data detailing the location of Earth. The contents were intended as a time capsule as well as an "interstellar message to any civilization, alien, or far-future human that may recover either of the *Voyagers*" (Nelson, 2021).

I've never been very savvy about constellations. Point at the night sky in Seoul and I mostly see pollution, anyway. It's crazy to think about how the *Voyagers* are actually traveling to the cluster of stars we have imposed meanings and stories to since prehistoric times. Camelopardalis, for instance, is a constellation in the northern sky that resembles a giraffe that some people in ancient Greece believed to have been a creature sent to the sky by Alexander the Great as a gift to their own king (Morgan, 1908). Camelopardalis is in a celestial sphere outside of the Milky Way, meaning many distant galaxies lie within the constellation's borders. In about forty thousand years, the *Voyagers* will approach the stars inside this constellation.

Imagine: The year is 42,021. Where to begin? You and I won't be alive. True to their name, the *Voyagers* will travel on, carrying remnants of our humanity into the gates of Camelopardalis. The Golden Records are the token of humanity as we saw it in 1977: the brief episodes, images, and sounds of what we believed to represent us. Among these symbols include greetings in fifty five languages that commonly translate to good wishes of peace and prosperity. There are various genres of music, from Mozart to Beethoven to rock music. Finally, there are also brainwaves of a woman in love (NASA, 2013). The record reveals to us concepts we *hoped* in the seventies to be universal and timelessly translatable: peace, love, and the transcendent power of art. However, were we to send to outer space another Golden Record today, I believe our messages and legacies would not be much different.

The Golden Record represents a lot of things: what we consider to be beautiful and unique in humanity, what things we hope are universal to all intelligent species, and a reminder of what all humans hold in common. Reflecting on these messages provides invaluable clarity on what unites us in an increasingly divisive time. Inspired by the Golden Record's message, in this chapter, I want to talk about tools that can help us connect to one another and reconnect to our own humanity in ways laws, institutions, and education cannot.

As I learn of international politics at school, I am often reluctantly convinced by the current system. In crude terms, international politics is often a power play: a showdown between big guns, big armies, and loud-mouthed leaders. Sure, this is one side of human politics, but I am more convinced that guns and grating tweets could only maneuver politics temporarily, and there is a greater potential in "soft power" to bring states together in a more tactful, compassionate, and permanent way.

Joseph Nye, who first introduced the concept of "soft power," describes soft power as the ability to influence the behavior of others by making others want to co-opt it or adopt an idea for its own use (Nye, 1990). It is contrasted with "hard power," which is influencing the behavior of others through coercion and payment.

For instance, the United States and the Soviet Union coerced with nuclear weapons in the Cold War and, more recently, China and the United States are trying to pressure each other's actions by using economic sanctions in the ongoing trade war. Soft power's instruments are different. Nye presents "culture" as one principal instrument of soft power (Nye, 1990).

Culture is often the underdog, overlooked and underestimated by the efficiency of lethal weapons and harsh sanctions. Culture is not just a political tool; it is a celebration of our diversity, of every nationality, and of every individual's contribution to the human story. Thus, soft power broadly, and culture in particular, is a powerful principle of positive engagement among states and communities. Culture is a rather broad term, defined by the Oxford Dictionary as "the customs, arts, social institutions, and achievements of a particular nation, people, or other social group" (Oxford, 2021).

In this chapter, I will use sports, food, and art as important components of cultural diplomacy. The power of these tools collectively is influential to not only improving international relations but also people-to-people relations.

Sports is a presiding example of how culture connects communities in ways institutions cannot. Even if I don't consider myself a huge sports fan, there is something magical in watching the Russian figure skater flawlessly execute an axel jump, and it is incredibly inspiring when a less-recognized national soccer team scores a goal against the Brazilian soccer team. Sports diplomacy itself is a widely studied field in international politics. For instance, in East Asian politics, a region fraught with historical tension, sports have helped "grease the wheels of diplomacy and engagement" according to studies written by Victor Cha, former director for Asian affairs in the White House's National Security Council (Cha, 2002). One example I personally found intriguing from attending Dr. Cha's classes is how sports improved North Korea's foreign relations.

North Korea's alienation is extreme and is often referred to as the "Hermit Kingdom." It does not engage in foreign relations as openly as other countries in its region or the rest of the world. Its radical alienation is caused and demonstrated by its totalitarian rule by a single dictator, the possession and development of nuclear weapons, the active-duty army that is the fourth largest in the world, and the human rights violations and abuses the United Nations describes are of "gravity, scale, and nature unparalleled in the contemporary world" (OHCHR, 2014). I think of North Korea as an "alien state" because of its political and living environments unlike any other in this world. It survives with fanatical values and behaviors, led by leaders who are unpredictable and largely unknown, and completely closed off from the rest of the world, much like an unapproachable planet in a faraway galaxy could be. I grew up never having met a single North Korean in my entire life.

I got to witness the power of sports on the Korean peninsula firsthand only a few years ago. In a moment of great celebration, sports reunified the Koreas (albeit briefly) and opened the doors for long-term positive North Korean interaction with international institutions. During the 2018 Pyeongchang Winter Olympics, the two Korean nations, aliens to each other for sixty years, marched in the opening ceremony with a unified flag (Vandenburg, 2019). The biggest events were the games that included the single, unified Korean women's ice hockey team that played in the Olympics, composed of a multitude of Korean identities around the world: North Koreans, South Koreans, Korean Americans, and Korean Canadians. I remember cheering for this super-Korean women's ice hockey team live on TV with my family—even as they lost every match! Despite having Koreans from various corners of the world, the team represented a united South and North Korea, the Korea we once had before the Korean War and the Korea that doesn't require the "South" or "North" prefixes. Korea was united. Given our countries are still at war, the moment was symbolic and unprecedented.

Women's ice hockey paved the way for future joint efforts of Korean collaboration—all thanks to sports.

The list of cooperation is growing, including joint Korean teams in the 2018 World Table Tennis Championships, mutual requests to send joint teams to 2021 Tokyo Summer Olympic Games, and a joint bid to host the 2023 FIFA Women's World Cup (Vandenburg, 2019). What many believed would be a beautiful but temporary moment of unification and peace in the 2018 Olympics survived to become something larger. Sports have paved the way for two enemy countries to cooperate and have given reasons for peace to prevail on the peninsula. Sports show even in the face of the most aggravating political conflict—an ongoing war with erratic nuclear threats—we can be on the same side.

Another example of soft power diplomacy is culinary diplomacy. The Golden Record does not specifically depict the types of food we eat in its contents, but it contains a photo of three people demonstrating licking, eating, and drinking (NASA, 2021). Scientists and anthropologists believe our metabolism distinguishes our species, both on Earth and in space (Denning, 2018). Our metabolism is a unique mark of our biological evolutionary path and thus shapes who we are and unites us. As humans, we all eat, taste, and metabolize the same way. Beyond its basic function, food is also an instrumental tool in diplomacy.

Food is a favored and neutral method of diplomacy by nations because of its simplicity. American Ambassador Ralph Samuel Thomas of Jamaica hailed culinary diplomacy's opportunity to develop trust in a relationship between two nations or two people. He said, "Food can definitely be a medium that allows people to interact in a more relaxed environment. People are very social animals, and during a meal, people tend to become far more relaxed" (Bjerklie, 2016). When describing his experience with food around the world, he is reminded how food can both represent its original cultures while taking on new forms, shapes, and tastes by its host country. Fusion cuisine is loved and popularized; the California sushi roll, kimchi quesadilla, or General Tso's chicken are examples of cross-cultural inventions and even represent historical relations between different communities. In such ways, food becomes a language of peaceful communication.

The Golden Record assumes when aliens do see our eating, licking, and drinking, they may understand its meaning. Of course, aliens (or even future-humans) could metabolize differently than we do. Some futurists predict food will be a thing of the past in our own inevitable future when supplements will be healthier and more "efficient" alternatives for our survival. Lo and behold, Silicon Valley entrepreneurs have already begun the development of "meal pills" (Widdicombe, 2014). But I'm not excited for this future. I lament the day my grandmother's famous spicy vegetable stew becomes too "inefficient" to enjoy. A world that cannot enjoy the simplicity and beauty of food is truly a world that has lost one of the greatest gifts of human creation. I believe most of us would choose a proper meal (and some dessert) shared with loved ones over a meal pill, and scientists think the same will hold true in the future (Widdicombe, 2014). Our consumption of food is an integral part of our social life and will continue to exist as an essential tool for communication, connection, and diplomacy.

Finally, there is diplomacy through art. Art is the most noticeable content of the Golden Record. There are over ninety minutes of music from a diversity of cultures in the phonograph as well as over 115 photographs that capture humanity (NASA, 2013). From classical music by Mozart to rock music to a night chant ritual by the Navajo Indians and panpipes music from local Solomon Islands musicians, there are harmonies from all corners of the world. The vast number of images contain representations of great human creations (The Great Wall of China and the Taj Mahal) to snapshots of nature (sand dunes and the sunset) to what we consider integral to life (the DNA structure, children, and family) (NASA, 2013).

When questioned about whether other intelligence, such as artificial intelligence, could create art like humans, the art community steadfastly denies it. One opinion voiced art is "an expression of human idea, emotion and filtered through personal experience and set against a broader cultural context," hence only art by humans can represent our identity, our culture, and our humanity (Weiner, 2018). Our belief that art is a key component of our humanity is also what makes it a powerful tool to connect people from all corners of the universe. The Academy for Cultural Diplomacy describes art as "a medium through which cultural heritage and identity can be experienced and interpreted" (Academy, 2021). Its power for representing the different cultures existing on our planet is paired with its ability to create a "neutral platform," much like food and sports.

Korea is a great example of a country that has successfully utilized art in diplomacy and used art to increase their soft power. There is even a name for Korea's soft power, titled *Hallyu,* translated literally as the Korean wave. For instance, the Korean boy band BTS brings $3.6 billion into the South Korean economy annually. In 2017, it was even estimated around eight hundred thousand tourists—or 7 percent of all arrivals—credited BTS for their interest to visit Korea (Suntikul, 2019). Wantanee Suntikul of *The Diplomat* writes that BTS also exemplifies the power of grassroots "people-to-people" diplomacy in spreading soft power. Suntikul writes, "People-to-people diplomacy happens when positive feelings about a nation or culture are spread through shared experiences between individuals across cultural divides" (Suntikul, 2019). Not only can art be a positive influence on a country's reputation and economy but it is also a platform that brings people from all backgrounds together.

Personally, I noticed how music plays a huge role in spreading Korea's soft power when I attended my first K-pop concert, a BTS concert in New Jersey. I didn't know what to expect as I entered MetLife Stadium in the summer of 2019. Close to one hundred thousand tickets were available for the night, and it sold out. As the concert began, I couldn't believe my ears. The American audience sang and even *rapped* along to every song in my mother tongue. While the performance by BTS was spectacular, I was captivated by the power of *Hallyu* that unfolded before me. That was not the only time I experienced the power a single music group could have in introducing South Korean language and culture to non-Koreans.

Music also has the power to bring two unlikely people together. I've personally met a surprising number of people at unforeseen spots, from a coffee shop in Copenhagen to a corner bookstore in Washington, DC, who noticed I was Korean and opened up for a conversation with me. Many told me they began to learn Korean and grew a love for Korean culture thanks to BTS. Music unites people of all cultures, languages, and even abilities. At concerts, despite not being able to hear the same pitches as hearing people, deaf or hard of hearing listeners enjoy the vibrations. The latest UK Live Music Census found more than three million deaf fans attend live music events every year—with ticket sales increasing over 50 percent each year (Webster, 2018). Music has an amazing "people-to-people" diplomatic power to connect us in a way nothing else can. It has a way of making us feel vulnerable, heard, and comforted. It is undeniably an art that humanity has mastered and will long be a powerful tool that can help us connect in genuine ways.

Throughout our history, art and space have always had a strong bond. I've recently been introduced to "Spacemusic," a genre recognized as "a subgenre of new-age music and is described as 'tranquil, hypnotic and moving'" (Masterclass, 2021). In popular culture, there are movie soundtracks entirely inspired by space, such as the recognizable themes of *Star Wars*, *Star Trek*, *E.T.*, and Christopher Nolan's *Interstellar.* Music inspired by space can be grand, pompous, and powerful or tranquil, hypnotic, and moving. We can notice the relationship between space and artistic creation in our popular music today, from Lady Gaga's 2020 *Chromatica* album themed "extraterrestrial" to her performance in the 2020 Video Music Awards in alien costumes to even BTS's music (Smyth, 2020). Three BTS songs inspired by space, "Moonchild," "Mikrokosmos," and "134340," will be played during NASA's next journey to the moon scheduled to take place by 2024 (Yonhap, 2019). Timelessly, we write music dedicated to space, we listen to music about space, and we send music to space.

One of my favorite videos of astronauts in action is of Chris Hadfield, the first Canadian to walk in space, who recorded himself singing David Bowie's "Space Oddity" on the International Space Station. The mustached former colonel of the Canadian Armed Forces' surprisingly beautiful, delicate rendition of "Space Oddity" is a tribute to the power of music and of international collaboration in space. Bowie himself was so moved by the cover that he praised it as "possibly the most poignant version of the song ever created" (Ferreira, 2020). Fifty million people have now watched this video of Hadfield, who is thankful his message behind the performance is meeting an audience around the world. The video with Earth and the ISS as a backdrop carries many messages, from the power of human collaboration to the relationship between art and space. He recalls hoping to bring "art full circle" by allowing people to experience, without it being stated, "that our culture had reached beyond the planet" (Hadfield, 2021).

While on the *Voyager*, in the interstellar medium forty thousand years away, humanity can be sampled through a small twelve-inch disk, our humanity is much more complex on Earth. Our cultures are rich with different traditions, values, and languages. But at the same time, we are reminded by the *Voyagers*' mission that some parts of the human experience are uniform. The voices of skilled diplomats, the hundreds of thousands of fans gathered in New Jersey, the singing astronaut and his audience to even the most alien of us, like North Korean leaders, show us some tools undeniably bring us together. Sports, food, and art are just a few examples of how, even in times of adversity, we can come together.

Humanity at its most beautiful is creative and playful. Kept to ourselves, our beauties are meaningless. We are social creatures; we thrive in coexistence, in peaceful competition, and in exchanging innovative knowledge. Our beauty and idiosyncrasy can be translated to art, music, sports, food, dance, and other ways we share and celebrate our cultures. Many of these have been compacted onto the Golden Record, a testament to the idea we enjoy sharing what we pride most of ourselves, even with those in the vast and possibly unreachable space.

There is a reason we continuously send art, photographs, and other tokens of human culture on spacecrafts. We cherish our creations, our legacies, and we long to be heard and seen. While our human culture is diverse and celebrated, it is also incredibly fragile. In fact, it was partly in fear that our cultures wouldn't survive the test of time that they were put on the Golden Record. The President of the United States at *Voyager*'s launch in 1977 believed the Golden Records' message was an attempt at "survival." In the message Jimmy Carter attached to the Voyager, he wrote, "This is a present from a small, distant world, a token of our sounds, our science, our images, our music, our thoughts, and our feelings. We are attempting to survive our time so we may live into yours"

(NASA, 2013). I'm afraid every day we take our humanity for granted. We just need to be reminded of what we want to be remembered by and what we are most afraid of losing, no matter who we are in this world, to make everyone come together on this planet.

# PART 3

# RE-ENTRY

## CHAPTER 8

# WHY IS AMERICA TURNING SPACE AMERICAN?

---

What was the last movie you watched that had aliens in it?

I might not guess correctly what movie it was you watched, but I'm confident I'm going to guess something else correctly: the general plot and its main character.

Did it involve aliens arriving on Earth, more specifically in New York, DC, and San Francisco (with sprinkles of Shanghai, Tokyo, and London), and waging war and claiming lives until we defeat them? Was there a hero who united all of humanity and salvaged us from extinction? Was that hero an *American*?

From NASA's leading research and operations in space to Hollywood's production of grappling space movies (where every hero is an American and every alien attack begins in

New York City), America is the hub of the human-space narrative. We need to address the responsibility the American government and its space programs have as it leads humankind's future into space.

The largest space program and space agency led by the US government, NASA accounts for over 30 percent of the operational spacecraft currently in orbit around Earth (ArcGIS, 2021). America is not only a global leader in space programs but it is also the leader in soft power with regards to space exploration. It carries immense political and cultural power and upholds an indomitable reputation when it comes to space.

American history, culture, and mind-set are key reasons why we need to be wary about how the narrative of our future in space is written. Historically, America was one of the first countries to begin exploring space. First, there was the "Space Race" of the 1950s to 1970s when the United States and its Cold War rival, the Soviet Union, competed to achieve the first spaceflight capability (Werth, 2004). As a result of this Space Race, three American men became the first humans to land on the moon. To the American space program, this was considered a win—and a claim to compete in similar ventures in space exploration henceforth. While exploring space as a "race" produced fast outcomes, it established the tone of all future space explorations to be one of international competition. The American victory also enabled America to project problems present in American culture and mind-set onto American space exploration.

The Space Race is an ode to "Manifest Destiny," the widely held imperialist cultural belief in nineteenth-century

America that American settlers were destined to expand across North America (Leib, 1999). Today, Manifest Destiny is criticized for its encouragement of the entitlement and greed of the American settlers. Yet history is repeating itself: Americans regard the milestones in human space exploration as ones of patriotism and Manifest Destiny. After all, upon the landing of American astronauts on the moon, the American flag also landed on the moon. Historically, the planting of the flag is proof of a "claim" to something, such as a territory or land (Bartenstein, 2009). The US flag on Earth's only moon is revealing of how Americans perceive their journey to space—a conquest.

Did you know the first planting of the American flag on the moon was a political decision? While the image of the American flag is iconic and celebrated, the story behind its planting discloses why it wasn't representative of a globalist, collaborative mind-set to space exploration. Before the launch of the Apollo mission that landed Neil Armstrong on the moon, there was resistance to the flag planting from Switzerland and Brazil, whose collaboration with NASA contributed to the success of the mission (Platoff, 1993). Astronaut Michael Collins, who flew *Apollo 11* to the moon in 1969 along with Neil Armstrong, wrote in *Carrying the Fire* that the possibility of taking up flags of all nations was seriously considered, and someone even designed a rig to display them (Collins, 2009).

There was a growing call to place a United Nations flag on the moon, symbolizing the historic moment for the world and humans worldwide. However, several members of the US Congress felt opposed to anything besides the American flag. California representative Burt L. Talcott warned NASA administrator Thomas Paine during a meeting of the House Appropriations Subcommittee on June 6, 1969, "You might have some nice international implications by using somebody else's flag, but I think you would have some very bad internal reactions and a great reduction in funds for NASA if anything like that happened" (Simmons, 2019). Just to make sure Paine and NASA got the message, days later, Congress successfully added an amendment to a NASA budget bill prohibiting any flag except an American one from being placed on the moon (Simmons, 2019). In the eyes of the American government, *only* the American flag could fly on the moon.

The United Nations anticipated this problem of the American claim over the moon, as well as outer space, prior to the moon landing. Two years prior to the *Apollo 11* moon landing, the United Nations adopted the commonly known Outer Space Treaty. Article II of the treaty clearly states, "Outer space, including the moon and other celestial bodies, is not subject to national appropriation by claim of sovereignty, by means of occupation, or by any other means" (Platoff, 1993). The United States, a signatory to the treaty, could not overtly claim the moon. However, as symbolic as it would be to physically plant a national flag on the lunar surface, according to a comprehensive paper on the flag landing by NASA, it was nevertheless "an expression of triumph similar to the planting of a flag on Mount Everest or at the North and South Poles" (Platoff, 1993).

American culture produced the Space Race and thoughts of space as territory to conquer, despite the fact man's landing on the moon was an international accomplishment.

Anthropologist Denning points out this unique "American-centric" mind-set to space is reflected in popular culture on space exploration as well. In our interview, she pointed out *Star Trek*, produced by American media, is "just a commentary on race relations in the country" (Roddenbury, 2004). One study by Trinity College on *Star Trek: The Original Series* discusses how two recurring characters, Sulu (an Asian character) and Uhura (a Black character), are reduced to exoticism through "recklessly whipping a fencing foil around" and "singing and dancing seductively" in various episodes (Pullis, 2014). More interestingly, as the study points out, the series ironically robs racially marginalized characters of their individuality while simultaneously "attempting to address issues of race or racism by condemning racially prejudiced aliens" through the main character's (Captain Kirk's) soliloquies on aliens' racial intolerance (Pullis, 2014).

Despite attempting to criticize race relations in America, *Star Trek* struggles to be self-perceptive. Humans are the most prominent characters in the show, and white male humans occupy two of the three central roles. While their nonwhite subordinates are rendered invisible or exoticized, the captain's intolerance of overt racial prejudice allows him to appear accepting and without prejudice of his own (Pullis, 2014). Given the global success of the franchise for fifty plus years, how many of us know the *Star Trek* theme song by heart? Yet how many of us are questioning the norms of alienation it established each time we hum the tune?

The original *Star Trek* TV series was also a product of its time and reflected the Cold War relations between the United States and the Soviet Union when its original TV shows aired in 1966 (Sarantakes, 2005). In a 1967 interview with the screenwriter and producer Gene L. Coon, he divulged the Klingons, the ruthless, irredeemable antagonists of the show, were intended to reflect the Soviet Union, as "we have always played them very much like the Russians" (Sarantakes, 2005). The original plot goes that the Federation (the honorable protagonists meant to embody America) and the Klingons were engaged in a long, hostile confrontation that constantly teetered on the edge of full-fledged war (Sarantakes, 2005). Even in modern reboots today, the journey of the USS *Enterprise* (the main spaceship in Star Trek) perpetuates American heroism and the destined conquest. Recall the famous words of the USS *Enterprise*'s mission: "Space: the final frontier. These are the voyages of the starship *Enterprise.* Its five-year mission: to explore strange new worlds. To seek out new life and new civilizations. To boldly go where no man has gone before!" (Courage, 2021). The idea of space as a "frontier" is charged with vocabulary from the Manifest Destiny of nineteenth century, when the unfamiliar land on the continent was considered a "frontier" the Americans were destined to conquer, tragically justifying their genocide of the Native American inhabitants (Miller, 2008).

Yet the idea of needing to own land in space is not limited to the American people. I am afraid to admit, I once considered buying land on the moon. I was seventeen, a senior in high school who was desperately out of original ideas to ask someone to prom. I resorted to suggestions online, one of which recommended I try the grand gesture of purchasing, at just twenty dollars, an acre on the moon. I was intrigued, believing it was kind of romantic—"I got you the moon! Will you go to prom with me?"—but alas, I never got the nerve to ask the guy, which thankfully means no moon land for me. I dodged that bullet. Lunar real estate is still a burgeoning business with millions of customers—might I mention, a business owned by an American named Dennis Hope (Farnham, 2013). Bundled up in an attractive package of American individualism and the hungry American business mind-set, the conquest of space is uniquely driven by Americans.

Hope paved the way for "extraterrestrial real estate." He has sold over eleven million dollars' worth of land on the moon, or more accurately, sold "lunar land certificates" to an impressive list of clients, from Tom Cruise, John Travolta, and Nicole Kidman to three US presidents, George H.W. Bush, Jimmy Carter, and Ronald Reagan (Ennis, 2013). He once sold a "country-sized" plot of land of 2.66 million acres for $250,000 (Ennis, 2013). In 2011, he was offered fifty million dollars for the moon's north pole. Hope has also claimed Mercury, Mars, Venus, Jupiter's moon Io, and Pluto. By claim, I mean he declared he "owns" those planets with no legal authority to do so and decided he would begin selling their land plots. His market is booming. He has sold close to 10 percent of the moon so far to millions of people around the world—over six hundred million acres of land on the moon (Farnham, 2013).

The very same treaty that prevented America from overtly claiming the moon should prevent Hope from claiming and capitalizing lunar real estate as well. Hope believes he found the loophole to the 1967 Outer Space Treaty, as he is just an "individual" who owns the moon and the rest of our solar system, not a country. Hope, a resident of Rio Vista, California, is a businessman. He was struggling to make ends meet when he looked through his car window, saw the moon, and thought, "Now there's a lot of property" (Farnham, 2013). So far, he has faced minimal backlash and has never heard back from the United Nations after he sent a note laying claim to the moon and the other planets. This doesn't faze him: "I wasn't asking their permission. I was merely informing them of what I was doing" (Farnham, 2013).

I believe his way of thinking is problematic. I don't believe the moon is to be owned or should be owned. I dread the thought that one day my grandkids will look up at the night sky and think, "Ah! That's someone's land right there!" While Hope's business is not ratified, more problematic than his business is his view of space. He sees it as new land he can conquer because it is profitable. Hope speaks like an American settler of the Wild West in the nineteenth century.

Hope isn't the only one hoping to profit from space, as more and more businesses are looking for their piece of the pie. NASA is currently publicizing its campaigns to send the first woman and next man on the moon by 2024 as well as the first man on Mars within the next decade. These plans are in partnership with other American businesses, such as SpaceX, Blue Marble, and Virgin Galactic (Hambleton, 2020). Not surprisingly, privatized space businesses are hoping to capitalize on space tourism as well as space colonialism. CEO of SpaceX Elon Musk is a vocal advocate of building a human colony on Mars as early as mid-2025 (M.b., 2017).

It's inspiring these businesses are investing in the future—our future into space. The (rich, white, privileged) American businessmen (Elon Musk, Jeff Bezos, and Michael Colgalzier) need to carefully consider if they are pioneering an insensitive beginning of American space history in partnership with the American government. As leaders of space explorations, the billionaires can reduce space, the great platform for international, human collaboration, to a game of colonization. For instance, Musk has explained his mind-set on space colonization clearly: "If we can establish a Mars colony, we can almost certainly colonize the whole solar system" (Anderson, 2014). He has even compared the importance of reusable rocket ships with American colonization of North America through ships. Is it possible Americans are once again claiming land or territory that is not theirs to own or claim in the first place? Manifest Destiny is repeating itself before our very eyes.

Multiple scientists have told me the "True Space Age" is coming, as humankind ventures further into space within the next five years. Indeed, moments that are as historically significant as Neil Armstrong's walk on the moon in 1969 could occur within just four years. We must carefully consider who is leading us into this True Space Age. Should it be the all-white, all-male, "Billionaire Space Race" leading us (Hern, 2021)? Is it better led by the American federal government? For instance, if all accessible space is owned by Americans, what kind of diplomacy minefields does that create? What motives, norms, and prejudices are we carrying into space exploration?

We need to be wary of rushing to achieve the next moonwalk moment without regard of its consequences. The Trump administration has been a vocal advocate for militarizing space, as well relaunching a Space Race, specifically against China. Trump himself ordered NASA to land Americans on

Mars before China, politicizing space exploration (Riotta, 2019). Vice President Mike Pence announced the White House was directing NASA to expedite its program and land people on the moon by 2024, despite doubts on its achievability from the scientific community. He cut NASA's previous 2028 goal in half and ordered American astronauts to be on the moon "by any means necessary" (Riotta, 2019). The new Space Race has been officially acknowledged by the American government. Chief Financial Officer of NASA Jeff DeWit declared, "There is still a Space Race where we want our country to do it first," and said he wants "to see an American flag" on Mars first, not the Chinese flag (Mosher, 2019).

Since the change of administration to President Biden, who has replaced much of Trump's legacy in the White House, space remains a noticeable exception (Davenport, 2021). President Biden and Vice President Harris have provided wholehearted support to the Artemis program (even its controversial time line) and released various videos chatting to American astronauts on the ISS. Biden's White House Press Secretary Jen Psaki made the administration's position quite clear, declaring the US government is excited to "conduct new and exciting science, prepare for future missions to Mars, and demonstrate America's values" (Davenport, 2021). It's no surprise, given one of Biden's signature achievements during his vice presidency was his push to enlarge NASA's budget in 2010, authorizing cooperation with private sector players such as SpaceX and Boeing against the advice of skeptical members of the Congress (Kluger, 2020). Though we can expect Biden's vocabulary in space diplomacy to be one of less divisiveness, it's clear Biden has invested interest in ensuring American leadership in space exploration.

The twentieth century Space Race achieved results in a global state of nuclear threats and intense international competition. While it undeniably produced outcomes, we cannot deny the centralization of American in its achievements, such as the planting of the American flag. If America continues to lead our future into space, it needs to do so with recognition of America's troubling past with annexing frontiers. We cannot enter space in a race where space is the frontier to be chased after, which America is at the risk of doing. If we do so, all great forthcoming achievements—man's first landing on Mars, woman's first landing on the moon, and humankind's flight to Venus—will be marred with anthropocentrism and ethnocentrism and with complete disregard of the fact no one owns space. Out in space, America can set the tone of exploration as one for all of humankind, yet American politicians refuse to do this.

There are successful and more collective ways of exploring space, such as the European Space Agency, an intergovernmental organization of twenty-two member states dedicated to the exploration of space. ESA Director General Jean-Jacques Dordain credits international cooperation on ESA's success, as he said, "International cooperation—first among the Member States themselves and then with other space-faring nations—has been the key to this success story" (ESA, 2005). As the only space agency composed of multiple nations, it continues to build and launch rockets, satellites, and train astronauts from various nations. ESA has facilitated diplomacy between member states in the name of science and technology since its founding in 1975. Even on Earth, in the age of globalism, we are continuously understanding the benefits of international cooperation, a mind-set of community efforts, and allyship. Space is one great platform to exercise international cooperation and truly lead humanity's future by exploration and curiosity rather than conquest or ownership.

The stakes are high for the next milestones in our space exploration to be ones that exemplify the greatness of humanity, not of a single nation. Space needs to become the metaphor for international collaboration. We can't afford to step into space in a mind-set of fear, conquest, and race between nations. As America pioneers our next great manned missions into space through its businesses and NASA, it must consider the responsibility it bears as one nation with a troubled past, leading our future in space—representing all humankind. In space, nationality is merely a concept.

When you look at the moon, what do you see? Well, you're not looking at the same moon that has been with us from the beginning of our time. The truth is America has planted the overwhelming majority of flags on the moon—six American flags planted by American men on its surface (Mosher, 2019). Fifty years ago, the moon and space adopted red, white, and blue stripes for hungry American politicians and businessmen. Sometime since, we have accepted through mainstream media that reflected such a mind-set that perhaps America does have a claim to space. It's time to question such a mind-set and challenge those continuing to breed space programs onto the new stage primed for conflict. We need a reminder when Neil Armstrong landed on the moon, he declared, "That's one small step for a man, one giant leap for *mankind*" (AP, 2019). He most certainly did not say, "That's one small step for American man, one giant leap for American mankind." America should not continue to turn space American, for space cannot be owned.

When you look at the moon tonight, what do you see? A beautiful, glistening, full moon? A wistful, foggy night gently lit by the crescent moon? Or do you see an *American* moon?

CHAPTER 9

# SCIENTISTS' PRIORITIES AND MEETING IRON MAN

You eat some decent food, watch some mediocre TV, take a lukewarm shower, and go to bed. The next day, you wake up and turn on the news to one blaring headline: "Aliens Are Real."

That's the kind of literal premise the United States was expecting in 1989 as it directed the International Academy of Astronautics (IAA) to write "The Declaration of Principles Concerning Activities Following the Detection of Extraterrestrial Intelligence" (Landfester, 2011). More specifically, the protocol outlined principles in the case SETI (Search for Extraterrestrial Life) verified a detected radio signal was emitted by extraterrestrial intelligent life. I was surprised I'd never heard of this protocol. If there was a "How to Face Aliens 101" guidebook issued by the government, I thought I would have come across it before.

But as I have researched, I've realized no academic papers and accredited research explain what we should prepare for in the scenario we "discover" or "are discovered by" other intelligent species in space. Scientists are interested in different things. So what does the academic community really focus on in the question of life in space and what should we prepare for in our future in space according to experts?

To begin unpacking my curiosity, I first spoke with the president of the International Academy of Astronautics when it revised its protocol in the 1990s, Dr. Seth Shostak. Dr. Shostak told me the original protocol, which had been invented during the Cold War, was born out of necessity in a time of political rivalry. Hence, the protocol was birthed for one reason: to prevent the Soviet Union from taking advantage of the signal's discovery first. Little about the protocol delineated measures that dealt with the repercussion of alien discovery to the rest of the world. It was understandable, given the most important issue at the time was the bilateral competition between the two superpowers.

Since 1989, the protocol has been revised once in 2010. Dr. Shostak, who was also involved in the protocol's revision, explained there were three broad revisions in response to contradictions in the first protocol. Many were additions for scientific integrity as well as principles to make the protocol less exclusive to the United States and the Soviet Union. He summarized the revisions simply: "One, if you find a signal, check it out. Two, tell everybody. Lastly, don't send messages back until we've talked with the United Nations or some international body." In sum, make sure it's the real thing, keep calm while the rest of the world freaks the fuck out, and *please* don't piss off the aliens—all important revisions.

Dr. Shostak shared with me the finalized 2010 protocol, which I noticed also focused on international cooperation as well as transparency. For instance, the fourth principle says, "All data necessary for the confirmation of the detection should be made available to the international scientific community," while its final principle states, "In the case of the confirmed detection of a signal, signatories to this declaration will not respond without first seeking guidance and consent of a broadly representative international body, such as the United Nations" (SETI IAA, 2010). Not only were the revisions necessary to make the matter of alien detection less exclusive to the United States and the Soviet Union but the updated protocol also tried to regulate who sends a response to the aliens.

While the principles were fascinating, I couldn't help but notice the entire protocol was barely two pages long with only eight principles to instruct the world on how to respond in the case of alien discovery. What about principles on how to attempt communication or establish peace? What about finding common ground? How do we notify people without triggering masses to hide in bunkers and never come out? Alien Greeting 101 was simpler than I expected. This may be because many scientists in IAA, SETI, and the international community studying space believe alien detection and contact are not viable problems and not worth properly preparing for.

Dr. Shostak smiled with nostalgia when I asked about a time when SETI came close to a potential discovery of ETI. On my screen, his starry Zoom background of an image of the twenty-foot-wide SETI telescope dish pointed to the night sky told me how much he loves his job. The glint in his eyes as he answered my question revealed he was about to tell a story he would never get tired of retelling. In 1997, Dr. Shostak was having dinner with his family when, for the first time, he got a phone call from his boss at SETI notifying him a possible ETI radio signal was detected by a fellow SETI scientist, John Dreher. His heart thumped at the anticipation that the whole world would change for him, for humanity, with this one signal. *Could it be? Could it be?*

He received an excited phone call from the *New York Times* office who had found out and was ready to publish the breaking news to the rest of the world. At the same time, a massive TV crew arrived in the control room of the telescope that detected the signal. Unfortunately, when he arrived at SETI, holding his breath, he realized it was a mistakenly picked up signal from a satellite in Europe. He dropped countless dinners to run to SETI each time he was notified about a potential detection like that night, but it was never *the* signal. He stopped holding his breath, and so did the rest of the world.

Dr. Shostak explained the brief history of nations' interest in searching for aliens—including its quick descent. In the 1990s, as the first exoplanets were being discovered by astronomers, many countries were engaging in similar missions as SETI, including the Soviet Union and China. International endeavors and curiosity died down as scientists struggled to prove the existence of aliens whose signals may be trillions of miles away. Dr. Shostak donned a wistful smile on his friendly face as he told me today, most cultures believe extraterrestrial intelligent life is "silly" and an expensive endeavor. SETI, based in America, is one of few remaining operating institutes still focusing on the detection of alien life.

The reason for the lack of focus on alien life is a matter of funding and logistics. While the idea you will one day wake up to aliens declaring their presence in a futuristic spaceship hanging above skyscrapers in cities around the world is familiar through our digestion of science fiction, the reality scientists are preparing for is much less action-packed. Dr. Shostak believes aliens would be "twenty-five trillion miles away or 4.3 light-years away" from our nearest other star system, Proxima Centauri. Most star systems looked at by SETI are 100 light-years away, which means that their signals, never mind their physical presence, are not likely to reach us within our lifetime. This makes SETI's practice of detecting signals a very safe practice, in Dr. Shostak's opinion, but it also means scientists see little point in engaging with the possibility of alien life if they are so far away.

Other members of SETI, such as anthropologist Kathryn Denning, agree aliens are not the priority in the space community. When she spoke with me, she insisted priorities absolutely *should* lie elsewhere. She said, "I don't believe in the existence of ETI. It's a logical, scientific possibility, but not an actual belief for me." Like many other scientists focused on space, she differentiates possibility from personal belief. In other words, she personally doesn't believe they exist, but she acknowledges the possibility they exist scientifically. She urged me to switch the focus of my book to be about matters more relevant to the near future because, as she states, "We have more urgent questions in the next five to ten years."

Denning listed many matters in our interview: how we're going to handle ourselves in the solar system as we continue to expand our exploration, what we're going to do with the moon in terms of interstate politics, how we're going to handle Venus and Mars, and how we're going to handle asteroid mining. She told me, "These are urgent questions, and by comparison, the alien questions kind of end up taking a back burner." I began to wonder, Was she right?

Denning personally focuses her study on general space ethics and general space issues, as "this is where it matters." She said, "It matters even more for your generation than it does for mine because you're the ones who are going to have to deal with whether or not we sorted out orbital debris, whether or not we sort out property rights or space traveling rights." Indeed, a recent report by NASA declared the Department of Defense is tracking more than twenty-seven thousand pieces of orbital debris large enough to threaten human spaceflight and robotic missions (O'Neill 2021). Don't forget Dennis Hope, the shrewd businessman profiting from space real estate. Finally, a lucky (and rich) twenty-eight-million-dollar auction winner won a seat on the first Blue Origin flight along with Jeff Bezos in July 2021, sparking heated debate on who should get access to spaceflight as space tourism takes off (Harwood, 2021). It's no question these are all important concerns.

However, while ruminating on alien life that is still but a slight possibility is less tangible than space debris or space real estate, I disagree that it is not a question of urgency for our future. I cannot argue asteroid mining and space property rights are less eminent than the question of intelligent life, but even as a layperson with no scientific background on space, I see great value in contemplating a future where SETI or anyone else discovers we are not alone. There are world-changing questions to address anthropologically, sociologically, philosophically, as well as politically.

Denning's interview reminded me of the first few days of my journey writing this book when I met Mr. Stark.

I never thought I would meet Mr. Antonio Stark—better known to the world as Iron Man—in the flesh.

Yet there I was one bright morning, having successfully corresponded with Mr. Antonio Stark over email for over a week, nervously and curiously waiting at the coffee shop where we had agreed to meet for an interview.

It's important to clarify the difference between my Mr. Stark and the Mr. Stark we are familiar with. Antonio Edward "Tony" Stark, better known as Iron Man, is a fictional superhero in the Marvel Universe (Favreau, 2008). I was talking to an Antonio Stark, a young Korean man in his twenties who I was introduced to by a mutual friend. He is an accredited space policy analyst who works for the United Nations and other international institutions. He is also an ordinary guy who rode his bike to meet me and was sipping a latte.

Stark was my very first interview for my book. I was eager to talk to anyone who had any professional or academic background in space and got my first opportunity the week after I began writing. I was happily surprised when, through a mutual writer, I was introduced to Iron Man as my very first source of information. It seemed like a sign from the universe that the moment I decided to write a book dedicated to my brother, I was greeted by his favorite superhero to welcome me to the world of space. I wasn't necessarily welcomed more so than I was warned.

As we shifted our conversation on the possibility of intelligent life, Stark was skeptical about the premise we would ever meet them in our lifetime. He believed the closest possibility of interacting with extraterrestrial life-forms was "bacterial lives on Mars and microbiological life-forms in the solar system." As a matter of fact, only a few weeks after our interview, scientists came out with the shocking discovery of phosphine gas, a possible marker for microbial life, on Venus (Chang, 2020). According to Stark, discovering actual sentient, biological life was like trying to think of sports cars in ancient Egypt when we had yet to build a pyramid. Any questions or topics pertaining to alien life were better left written about in a fictional manner to be truly relevant to our life. After talking to Stark, I felt depleted and disillusioned. Could he be right? Was there no point in writing about aliens?

I returned to my thoughts on why I decided to write about space, aliens, and positive engagement in the first place. The first reason was quite simple: it was rooted in my own life experiences. I was tired of learning engaging with "aliens" or "others" in our past and present was a means to an end, a way to gain profits or "win" at the cost of other life.

I was born in South Korea in 1999. On an individual level, I have never experienced active war, but even today, South and North Korea are still at war in the form of "frozen conflict"

(Nam, 2021). These conflicts are frequent—from bombings to kidnappings to shootings—and have cost hundreds of South Korean and unknown numbers of North Korean lives. On an international level, North Korea's precariousness and tensions on the Korean peninsula are central topics in diplomacy between the United States, South Korea, and other East Asian countries.

However, even as I live in a country at war, I feel incredibly privileged. For one, I was born after the Korean War reached an armistice, whereas my grandparents experienced childhoods marred by gunfights and deaths during the peak of the war. The biggest privilege of being born in a more peaceful country than my grandparents were is I can imagine peace. Because I was born after the Korean War and had the privilege of traveling to countries that have evolved beyond armed regional conflicts, peace feels more tangible than war and chaos. If it's a reality in another part of the world, what says the Korean peninsula also doesn't deserve a similar degree of peacefulness and prosperity? Even if the North and South are still at war today, I am convinced the most likely outcome of unification will be peaceful coexistence or peaceful unification.

In reality, peaceful coexistence does not fully reflect the situation on the peninsula, or even the rest of the world. Today, we are still marred in various humanitarian crises and wars. We can't seem to escape our pattern of threats, wars, and conflicts. Wars seem almost inherent to us, as if from the beginning of human history there has been violence and humanity was doomed from its beginning to be trapped in the game of winning and losing.

People's beliefs show differently. As I imagine a more peaceful future in my home, statistics show most Koreans think like I do. Studies show 40.5 percent of South Koreans think peaceful coexistence is the most likely outcome, while 31.6 percent said peaceful unification through dialogue and negotiations is the most probable endgame (Lee, 2020). People are not only more hopeful for peace but they also think it's a possible reality.

Like the future of Korea, space makes me hopeful. No, space makes me *excited* because it is like a blank canvas. We haven't engaged in conflict yet with the intelligent beings in space, or even against each other. When the future comes, even if it is thousands of years away, could we change what defines us by starting history on the right foot? Could space be purely a ground for peace and collaboration? Could our efforts of globalization and liberalism extend to the future protocol of space diplomacy? On the other side of wars and races, space is also a powerful instigator for collaboration.

Space reminds us of our humanity and connects us in times of division, which brings us to my second reason for writing this book. I wrote it for my brother, a curious and imaginative person with a great love of science fiction. Movies, TV shows, and story-telling games set in space are an infinite source of inspiration for my brother, and writing about it helped me feel more connected to him.

I also wanted to illuminate the gravity of space exploration in the world today to young, impressionable minds like his. Today, space is a blank canvas, but we may be closer than we think to polluting it with our habits of alienation, dehumanization, anthropocentrism, ethnocentrism, and fear. Such a future may only be a few years away as we engage in a "Space Race" to reach Mars, the moon, and other planets in our solar system. We must stop the Space Race from turning into a Space War.

"You're literally James Holden," Stark said, shaking his head at me. He was referring to the main character of the science fiction series *The Expanse* who is known for his idealism, tasked with saving the world (Corey, 2018). Some fans often call Holden the Jon Snow of the series, as both repeatedly (and often recklessly) act on their ideological beliefs. Like Jon Snow, I may know nothing (HBO, 2012). Some days when I write this book, I do question if my ideas of our future in space are uninformed and overly idealistic.

But I was reminded Stark himself shares a name with a fictional Marvel character, a man who sacrificed his life to preserve peace in the intergalactic universe.

Like James Holden, I'm imagining a new normal that some argue could never be our reality. It's a world my grandparents wished for but couldn't fathom. I dare to imagine a world with more compassion, collaboration, and connection. It's a world made up of James Holdens, Jon Snows, and Tony Starks.

I responded, "We need more people like him."

Scientists who are leading our future in space are focused on very different things than I am, such as the ramifications of human spacecrafts' orbital debris and our imminent futures on the moon, Mars, and Venus. That doesn't have to stop us from dreaming about and contemplating what lies ahead. To me, an urgent concern is we will negatively engage with extraterrestrial aliens with our history of prejudice and flawed political games. No time is as good to start preparing as now as we enter the True Space Age.

I simply hope we can protect space and our sense of wonder of what curiosities lie ahead without being disillusioned by the realities of human conflict. Even if it means I am imagining a wildly imaginative future, I see the value in exercising our muscles to picture the possibilities. Who knows, if only we had a few more people who were convinced we could do things differently outside of Earth's atmosphere, maybe the world would finally find peace—in space.

## CHAPTER 10

# SPACE JUNKIES AND STAYING IMAGINATIVE

As I sit here writing in my room, it's past midnight, and on the other side of the concrete wall sleeps the young boy who inspired my whole journey with space.

Thus far in my life as a twenty-one-year-old, there are few people who rely on me entirely, as most are young adults or elders with families of their own. Yet there is one boy who asks me every day to help him fill the gaps in life. He unreservedly asks me, and only me, endless questions. He aches to understand everything from facts about everyday life to the secrets of the universe. Small questions are raised from how to microwave frozen rice, why it's important to talk to our grandparents, how to help Mom feel better, but bigger questions come along just as often. These are inquiries I cannot as easily answer on demand, like what it means for us to be expatriates, why our planet only has one moon, and where we will go when we are dead. For him, no question is too menial or too big to be thrown my way.

I'm often reminded of who I am when he asks me these larger-than-life questions that I cannot answer off the top of my head. I pause and glance at the inquisitor—the child who asks, who has suddenly grown to be two heads taller than me when yesterday he was barely larger than the stuffed bear he slept next to in his cradle. The adult-sized kid looks down on me expectedly, and I see his wide-eyed wonder, the unconditional trust in his gaze, the anticipation that what I will say will be his gospel truth, and I am suddenly reminded of something both mundane and immense in the brief second before I respond. I am reminded I am his sister. Having a much-younger brother who has the depth of curiosity only a child can have, who for some reason has chosen to respect and trust me so wholeheartedly, reminds me being his sister means I am everything to him. In our home, where only I can communicate to him in English, closest to him in age, most similar to him in our experiences abroad, and his only friend in Seoul, I am his peer, mentor, conversation partner, and best friend.

I was never very close to my brother, given I left home to pursue a higher education in the United States when he was just eight. In fact, I'd only see him once or twice a year when I could fly back home during school breaks. Each time, he would grow a foot taller than when I had left him. His height, his voice, and his crouching demeanor made him more and more like a stranger to me.

By the strike of sudden global misfortune—the pandemic—we have been together from day one of quarantine in the early months of 2020 until today, January 2021. It is the most time we have spent together. Sometimes I forget, but other days I'm reminded by our inside jokes, deep conversations, and the rare (and relatively new) hugs that we have spent time together without being separated for the longest time in seven years.

I won't deny that it was rough at moments, given our differences. Me, barely an adult who had just turned the legal drinking age in the United States and who is in her final year in college, and him, a boy who had just turned sixteen, yet to begin high school due to a medical condition. We are opposites—two siblings headed in different directions. But I wouldn't hesitate to say spending time with him was the best thing that happened in 2020.

My brother taught me so much about this book before I even knew I was going to write a book on space. He was the one who sparked my curiosity at 3:00 a.m. in the first few months of quarantine when we shared a bed. When he couldn't fall asleep, he would turn to me and sneak in those big questions while I lay trying to sleep:

"Ellena, do you think there is a reason why we haven't met any aliens?"

"Ellena, would you travel to planets in different galaxies if it was possible?"

"Ellena, what do you think about the *Star Trek Discovery* series so far?"

"*What? You haven't watched it?* How could you not? You're not my sister!"

Every so often when my answers trailed off from fatigue or revealed my lack of knowledge in the most recent *Star Trek* series, he would blast YouTube videos on his favorite topics on an endless loop at maximum volume in the small room we shared. I would be forced to listen to the passionate voices of space fanatics, citizen scientists, or conspiracy theorists and be exposed to the different thoughts people around the world had on space.

Here is the really wonderful thing about my brother: there are few people in my own life who are as unafraid to imagine as him. It seems every day he travels the entire universe five, ten times through his thoughts. Perhaps every child possesses such formidable curiosity, but there is really only one kid in my life, and it's him—and his unbridled curiosity. Some may call him childishly imaginative, but I call what he does "brave wondering." He dares to question the unknown, seek answers for questions bigger than himself, our planet, or even our galaxy. He is not daunted by the fact our intelligence and technology are yet unable to provide satisfying answers. He continues to look for answers on YouTube, Reddit, social media platforms, blogs, and any other non-traditional outlets for acquiring knowledge. I know plenty of people who, when faced with a difficult question, give up on the spot or lose interest.

Inspired by his curiosity and equipped with a college education, I've personally looked far and wide for the answers to space in more traditional outlets. From asking astrobiologists who work in respected science institutions to professors at universities to scientists at NASA, I've had the great opportunity to ask questions to these experts that my brother had been hoping to acquire. I've also had opportunities to talk to space junkies like my brother from people who had blogs, podcasts, and books of their own on the topic.

The humble discovery I have made is there is no right or wrong way to think about space, except on one aspect: to stay curious and imaginative. There are vast differences between space as a field in science and academia and space as a limitless thought experiment for the layperson. Something I found astonishing from my experience talking to people on opposite ends of the whole spectrum was that often, ordinary people like you and me are more outspoken when it comes to staying curious about space than scientists, professors, and other experts.

What does space inspire in you?

For example, my friend Yeji, who is a physical therapist but an avid fan of space theories, believes we all live in parallel universes. When I ask her about her opinions, she answers without hesitation that she believes in galaxies far away from ours, unreachable by human travel, there exists different versions of her being. She has thought the possibility through and through and expands on her theory by saying in one different version of herself, she may have pursued her childhood dream of being an airplane pilot instead of going down the path of physical education she was forced onto by her parents. The idea of space reflects her ideas of regret, hope, adulthood, and choices. She tells me she could talk for days on end about space and the various imaginations it evokes for her.

Another friend, Ariel, a college student just like myself, believes in "dark matter." Her eyes light up as she explains how much potential lies in this one concept, what some scientists believe accounts for the unexplained motions of stars within galaxies (O'Neill, 2021). According to renowned astrophysicist and planetary scientist Neil deGrasse Tyson, it also makes up for the "bulk of a galaxy's mass and forms the foundation of our universe's large-scale structure" but remains a concept scientists are still mostly in the dark (haha) about. She was introduced to dark matter by a 2017 Neil deGrasse Tyson book called *Astrophysics for People in a Hurry*, and she urges me to consider the endless possibilities that lie ahead if it turns out to be scientifically true. She's a dancer, a writer, and a photographer; she's an artist with a mind as creative and expressive as her passions. In her free time, she enjoys reading and talking about space with her friends and families. Space in Ariel's voice reflects her powerful spirit of wonder, possibilities, and freedom.

To my mother, who religiously watches documentaries on the History Channel that explain aliens, space is a vehicle to understand great human achievements. From pyramids to language to math to technological revolutions, Mom believes all the great advancements by humans on Earth have been bestowed on us by superior intelligent beings from outer space. She believes in time travel, believes aliens have visited us, and believes aliens still live among us. She most recently became convinced the tallest tower in Seoul that was just erected a few years ago, the Lotte Tower, is a new headquarters for aliens. To her credit, the tower stands stark amidst the already sky-high city skyline in two parallel planes that arc in the tip to meet—much like the eye of Sauron in the Dark Tower in *Lord of the Rings* (Tolkien, 1991). My mom's eyes light up every time we drive past the tower or spot it at a distance high up on a mountain trail. Although I personally don't believe many of her theories she candidly shares, I love how I can always rely on space as a mutual ground for conversation to spark curiosity and lift her mood when she is down.

My brother is a huge Marvel, *Star Wars,* and *Star Trek* fan. He loves immersing himself in the world of multiverses and superheroes. He loves all adventures set in space, but he particularly enjoys tying them back to science that exists already in the field of space. Often, he shares with me the theories that some scientists hold as a hypothesis for why "aliens" aren't real yet. The list is long, including the Rare Earth Theory, Great Filter Theory, Great Silence Theory, Early Bird Theory, Different Kind of Life Theory, and In a Far Away Galaxy Theory. To my brother, space is a blank canvas for him to paint the secrets of our universe on—for him to wonder, to escape the everyday frustrations of growing into a young adult coupled with a medical condition exacerbated by the global pandemic. Space is there for him at the end of the day, welcoming him in its darkness and light for him to find solace and wonder.

In all my experience talking to people close and far, through Zoom and in person, about what may lie ahead in the grand journey between human and space, it became clear no one believes in one thing. Everyone holds different beliefs, espouses disparate theories, and pictures various hopes and dreams. There is a diversity of questions about what it means to be alive on this planet Earth in this infinitely vast universe. Every conversation is unique, and every conversation is full of life. People believe in space. Perhaps in a world where so many variables are out of our control and full of moments when we lack conviction, we depend on space to provide us inspiration and hope. It has certainly done its part for my friends and family.

In such a way, humanity is dependent on space as a blank, amorphous canvas, and I feel protective of it to stay that way. It's embarrassing to admit, but I personally have been greatly disillusioned through the research and interviews with the people who are "experts" and "scientists" in this field. They see space as a field for studies and science, and their tones have often been dismissive of the curiosities and hypotheses of the laypeople. They have urged me there is no time for it, no place for it, and that it is certainly a waste of my time and energy. I don't agree.

Astrophysicists, anthropologists, astronomers, and space policy analysts have all told me what exactly lies ahead in five and ten years, and the reality—as outlined in early chapters—is messy. Some are expectant, such as more chaotic and possessive human politics, more disagreements to comb through, and more clashes in beliefs, directions, and biases. In reality, space is not as simple or as hopeful as we hope it may be. There is something to learn from the unbridled imagination of everyday space enthusiasts. You can dismiss them as crazy, but their "curiosity/imagination" muscles are *strong*, and you can build up your own muscles, too.

We aren't alone when we think of space. We are more naive, gullible, and optimistic than we think. Yes, these qualities are accompanied by the lack of information of what is out there, but when have discovery and information ever presented an obstacle to our growth? There is power to imagination, and we must remember that.

For all out there who are passionate about space, for all who hold theories, especially those young and infinitely curious like my brother, I hope you keep exercising your muscles for wonder and imagination. There will only ever be as much to hope for as there are people who envision it and have the potential to actualize it. My brother dreams one day he will be able to work for a space agency, continuing to exercise his curious and imaginative mind. He is especially interested in the intersection between nanotechnology and space exploration technology. The idea our future is firmly rooted in space is a no brainer. That our future in space is one full of optimism, wonder, and exploration, on the other hand, is not guaranteed.

My favorite quote from climate futurist and planetary thinker Alex Steffen, who explores humanity's long-term relationship with our planet including sustainable development and climate activism, boldly declares hope is a political act. He says, "Optimism is a political act. Those who benefit from the status quo are perfectly happy for us to think nothing is going to get any better. In fact, these days, cynicism is obedience" (Steffen, 2006). Optimism without purpose prevents progress, but optimism with purpose could be a political act, like Steffen suggests. In the face of darkness, can we be radically optimistic?

We have a lot to gain from radical optimism, the practice to combat cynicism and denialism and see optimism based on reason and evidence, even if it's buried under the negative facts. It's a practice many climate activists take on, for the discussion of the climate crisis is often dominated by terrifying statistics. They assert if we decide climate change is simply too big a problem for us to tackle, we have given up hope. Former United Nations climate chief Christiana Figueres says, "What we do and how we do it is largely determined by how we think. While there is never a guarantee of success at any challenge, the chances of success are predicated on our attitude toward that very challenge" (McMahon, 2020). We have much to gain from radical optimism for humanity's future in the True Space Age, another field whose future can easily feel too large for us to be in control of.

Without optimism, we have everything to lose. To quote UNFCC, the United Nations body that has led global activism for climate change, we must be radically optimistic "to rise to the next level of our abilities, because it's necessary to do so, and because together, we can" (Global Optimism, 2021). The same rings true for global activism for space exploration. We are on the brink of new discoveries beyond the final layer of Earth's atmosphere, along with them a flood of minefields. We will have to navigate political tensions such as nations staking a claim to extraterrestrial property, ethical questions on whether it is right to exploit other planets' resources and extraterrestrial lives, and so many more.

Some of these matters will feel beyond your reach, beyond mattering to your everyday life. Perhaps you will choose to believe the mistakes we make in space and the conflicts tethered to them are inevitable. But don't dismiss space with cynicism or a false sense of realism. I urge you to develop your own opinions on space and on what you believe is wrong and right. Just as you have a responsibility to fight climate change as a resident of this planet, you have a responsibility to space issues as a resident of this universe. Protect space by staying outspoken on your opinion on space. Stay radically optimistic that humanity in the True Space Age will be defined by our own actions. Finally, know your voice matters.

At my weakest, I am cynical. Cynicism is like a sneaky shadow, following our every move, just one step behind, waiting for the perfect moment to attack. It punches me in the back with guile, and I am swiftly on the ground, winded. In such moments, I can never believe in anything—not in humanity, not in the future, not even my friends or myself. It takes all my strength to be optimistic again, almost like I'm trying to work a weak and long underused muscle in my mind and heart. After I awaken my optimism, I stand again on my two feet and the world seems clearer than before. I can believe again, imagine again, and I can love again.

Occasionally, my brother falls victim to cynicism, and it hurts to see someone I love weakened by the darkness. His condition makes it even harder to escape the rut, and as much as I want to help him, I'm painfully aware he must get out on his own. One of those times, as I tried to cheer him up, he asked me in exasperation, "Ellena, how do you stay so optimistic?"

I didn't know how to respond then, but if he asks me again, this is what I will respond with: "Every one of us possesses the muscle of optimism. It's just a tricky one to exercise."

I also encourage you to work that muscle as often as you can, to expand it in the face of cynicism.

## CHAPTER 11

# LIVING IN THE UNKNOWN

As we near the end of our journey, I invite you to return to where we first met. The warm sand tickles your toes, the waves' gentle crash accompanying the breeze of the ocean. We return to the familiar presence of Bruce Robinson and Octomom, who ushered us into space by teaching us the hard-earned rewards from boldly diving into the unknown (McEwan, 2020). We have ventured into the unknown, farther and deeper, page by page, from the deep sea with Bruce to the gaseous surface of Venus with space scientists, to many, many galaxies away with *Voyager 1*. We return to this shore, at last, with a profound understanding.

We are imperfect explorers.

We often explore, struck by curiosity, but guided by our politics and prejudice. We explore with predetermined ideas of who is the explorer and who is the explored. We are an intelligent and inquisitive species, but we do not always think through the consequences of our explorations for those who are not on our journey. We have yet to perfect the tools of engagement or shed our instincts to dehumanize and alienate. What's more, if the desire is to explore the unknown, we often mistake our destination.

We realize sometimes we discover an unknown back on our own planet—from the Middle East to North Korea, even in our neighborhoods and in our own family. There are still mysteries here on Earth that we must understand, countless secrets to unpack and skills to hone. There will always be unknowns. There are "aliens" here on Earth, for each of us cursed by our history of violence and blessed by the diversity that is humanity.

It's never been ambiguous to me why we explore space when it comes to scientific reasons. Overcoming the challenges of space exploration has bestowed on us various technological advancements from aviation technology to vaccine research. But what is the deeper reason we want to explore space? I'm reminded of what an anthropologist told me: in all our efforts to reach outer space, we are learning mostly about ourselves, much more than we are learning of what lies out there. Perhaps it's inspiring to feel the greater unknown because the more we can learn about ourselves, we can bring ourselves closer and awaken ourselves to a fuller and more connected life. Ultimately, perhaps we explore to belong.

It's no coincidence we relate most strongly to stories of space exploration narrated through the human voice: stories of the first woman who will finally land on the moon fifty five years after twelve men have already walked on its surface, and the hopes of people from 159 nations who bid for a seat on the first reusable rocket to carry civilians (Helmore, 2021). We empathize, and we envision flying off into space, even if we aren't the chosen ones landing on the moon in 2024 or launching into space on a pilot-less reusable rocket with Jeff Bezos in 2021. No milestone in space is a lone accomplishment of just one person. Spaceflight is the pinnacle of the human effort; countless ideas, nations, and people come together to overcome obstacles and compensate for each other's shortcomings to achieve the impossible. When we watch those rockets fly off into space after the nerve-racking countdown, we celebrate as if it was our very own friend on that spaceship. Through space, we feel more connected.

When in the rare breakthrough moments we learn about the true "others" beyond our star, we are more united than we were before. In 2020 alone, we learned there is a possible signature of life on Venus, discovered a million new galaxies, and we conceived there are 1,004 star systems capable of seeing Earth within 326 light-years. We also found out that one star just twelve light-years from Earth will be in a position to see Earth in 2044 (Letzer, 2021). These discoveries remind us we are but one planet in an ecosystem of trillions and trillions. This can be a lonely and scary fact, but we find solace in knowing we aren't alone in this experience. The human experience is a song all seven billion of us dance to, even if the melody differs by tongue and tribe. Space reminds us of this fact.

Back on the shore of Monterey Coast, I think of Octomom. I think of how all our explorations are connected. Our introduction to her life changed the deep-sea exploration field forever, but her planetary record for a brooding period even contributed to the field of space exploration. There's a special connection between the deep sea and space, so it's no wonder her story spoke for scientists studying deep space.

Deep sea and deep space were both habitats assumed to be lifeless wastelands. Temperatures are barely above freezing, there is crushing pressure in both places, and for the deep sea, even sunlight fails to penetrate so far below. Yet, the fact there is burgeoning life miles under the sea's surface, such as Octomom, proves there could be life in similar conditions on other planets. In fact, NASA has dedicated a large project for this very reason: Project SUBSEA, which stands for "Systematic Underwater Biogeochemical Science and Exploration Analog." The project blends ocean exploration with ocean worlds research to address knowledge gaps related to the origins of life and the habitability potential of other planets in our solar system (NOAA, 2018).

NASA often calls the oceans The Great Unknown (Dunbar, 2009). Indeed, our own planet's ocean and the deep sea are barely researched or known to us. Seventy percent of our planet is the ocean, and 90 percent of our ocean is the deep sea. Most of the ocean remains unexplored, and the deep sea's creatures and their lives are still a mystery (NOAA, 2009). We are living in a world of unknowns, and, somehow, each exploration and discovery connects to the other.

Water, a sign of life, is multi-planetary in our solar system. Robotic envoys on Jupiter's moon Europa and Saturn's moon Enceladus in recent decades have made discoveries that support SUBSEA. Both moons have vast liquid water oceans sloshing beneath their icy crusts. Sunlight likely doesn't reach below the thick ice sheets coating the moons, and if the chemically rich vent environments exist on those alien ocean worlds, they could fuel deep-sea life there too (Northon, 2017).

Such parallels between Earth and space make me wonder what the next chapter of the human story will be as we enter the True Space Age. There are patterns of humanity—violence, discrimination, colonization, anthropocentrism—I pray are not reflected by other intelligent species in outer space. Will unforeseen discoveries in this period prompt our greatest potential or trigger our darkest doom? Will it be what some experts warned is a true possibility—unimaginable violence, conflict, and war? How can we ensure we don't needlessly arouse our ugliest temperaments in this process?

In such moments of doubt and fear, I return to Bruce and Octomom. Five thousand feet below land, Bruce found a life that spoke to him, and that story spoke to him with humanity and compassion.

Perhaps there are things more universal than we would like to believe: motherhood, sacrifice, and compassion.

Of course, there are creatures on Earth that ostensibly lack these mind-sets. Spiders eat their young, and cuckoo birds abandon their eggs. But even if it's just one species out there capable of compassion, deep in our ocean or deep in outer space, isn't it also a possibility? I say yes. Driven by fear of the unknown, exploration becomes a trap of our own making. Instead, I hold onto hope, for even in my short life, thus far,

I have tasted the spectrum of life here on Earth and understood how rare it is for the unknown to not return to us with wonder and compassion if one prepares for it. Though not all of us will be the lucky captains behind the helms to manifest those journeys in deep space, we can still be inspired by the explorers who do fly into the unknown and make contact right here on Earth.

Bruce is one such explorer who inspires us. He saw humanity in this octopus and spent years studying and spending time with her. It's that empathy we are returning to. He showed us we can see beyond the anthropocentric world.

Humanity is a double-edged sword. Humans can destroy like no other creature on this planet. What other species sabotages other species (as well as its own) and environments with such ease on a massive spectrum, brandishes injustice for greed, and murders for its own appetite? If such markers define humanity, anthropocentrism would be the surest way to our self-destruction right here on this planet, forget ever evolving into a space-faring species. However, while it's a fact we are capable of the greatest evils on this planet, the contrary is equally as true.

In this book, I explored what I believe is the true definition of humanity: our diversity of cultures, beliefs, languages, and life experiences; our joy in imagining, creating, and sharing; our ability to actively hope, be patient, and cognitively empathize; our will to collaborate and socialize; and finally, our inclination to sacrifice ourselves in the name of love as well as our choice to protect the vulnerable and empower the underdogs. Take away even one of these markers, and you are left with a shell of humanity—an intelligent, destructive machine. Though the virtues of the human species should never be forgotten in our everyday life, it must unquestionably define our endeavors in outer space.

When we are faced with what is truly foreign for the future of our humanity—the extraterrestrial—we need to be equipped with the proper tools. Advance with weapons of mass destruction or hard power politics and we will fail to guarantee positive relations between another species. We must prepare most principally with our humanity, most importantly, with the powers of collaboration, cooperation, and compassion. No matter how unpredictable or far away this moment of engagement is, you and I can also prepare for this voyage, beginning right here in this moment.

I am human; therefore, I am prejudiced. Biases and discrimination are part of who we are and what has historically reduced us to cold, killing machines and incredibly imperfect explorers. There's a word we use to describe this initial process of discrimination. This neat word describes our active inhibition from compassion. In fact, the word is defined literally as "the loss or lack of sympathy."

The word is alienation.

So inscribed into our language, our mainstream media, and our actions, we approach the foreign with suspicion and immediately jump to labeling it as a threat to our survival. We alienate immigrants, races, sexes, cultures, and anything we cannot identify with. We alienate across the corners of Earth and even to what is foreign to us in the corners of the universe. It's the greatest paradox: we want to belong, yet we alienate.

There is a source of political power that is repeatedly overlooked: our ability to empathize and love. This untapped potential of our humanity calls for a restructuring of domestic politics (politicians exploiting our fear of others for votes), foreign relations (soft power and cultural diplomacy), and even our day-to-day lives between humankind and other Earthly species (escaping anthropocentrism and focusing on ecocentrism). We need to paint a future that is brighter than our past. We need to build relations based on what we have in common, not on what differentiates us. Most importantly, we need to envision and speak our mind—for how it should be and what could be.

We are imperfect explorers, but it is our destiny to explore. It's impossible not to, for the unknown beckons from everywhere. As we gaze up above beyond the clouds, beyond the blue sky, the silent waters of the cosmic ocean welcome us still, reminding us we belong in this perennially old and vast ocean. It's not a question of if we belong that we gravitate to. We feel the pull of the wider universe, even if we can't see it. Back on Earth, we attune to the murmur of strangers' chatter, the hoarse wail of California gulls, and the low boom of a fishing boat's horn further offshore. Each sight, sound, and smell carries stories of lives we do not know. It's the question of where.

You ask me impatiently still: So now that we have all the tools to discover the unknown, *where exactly* should we be looking? Out in space? Or here on Earth? What are we looking for? Aliens? Secrets to unlock the universe? A greater purpose?

For now, the answers matter less than how we explore. Cherish your curiosity, protect your sense of wonder, and explore freely with empathy. Maybe one day, we will all make discoveries on the edge of the universe that will change everything for good, but today, we begin here on this shore. Every wonder is just one dive away, but let's not haste to the destination lest we forget where we begin and what the voyage will be.

Most importantly, there is no need to rush to seek the unknown, for there is one timeless truth about you and me:

We have, and always will, live in the heart of the unknown.

# ACKNOWLEDGMENTS

In creating this book, perhaps through my brazen insistence as a journalism student or perhaps by a stroke of luck, I got the amazing opportunity to interview people who have dedicated their lives to advancing the study of space. Each conversation taught me there is always more learn about our universe. Thank you to all the space experts and space junkies around the world who accommodated my nightmarish math with time zones.

I want to especially thank the following experts for sharing your journey with space and your knowledge in your respected fields:

**Dr. Seth Shostak**—American astronomer and author. Currently the senior astronomer for the SETI Institute. Former chair of International Academy of Astronautics' SETI Permanent Study Group. Host of *Big Picture Science* podcast.

**Dr. Katheryn Denning**—Associate Professor of anthropology at York University in Toronto. Collaborated with the NASA Astrobiology Institute and the SETI Institute and is a longtime member of the SETI Permanent Study Committee of the International Academy of Astronautics.

**Dr. David Catling**—Professor in Earth and space sciences at the University of Washington. Planetary scientist and astrobiologist. Participated in NASA's Mars exploration program and contributed research to help find life elsewhere in the solar system. Author of *Atmospheric Evolution on Inhabited and Lifeless Worlds* and *Astrobiology: A Very Short Introduction.*

**Dr. Graham Lau**—Research scientist at Blue Marble Space Institute of Science, a US-based international nonprofit that promotes cooperative exploration of space, examines life as a planetary process, and enables a sustainable future on Earth.

**Nathan Price**—President of NSS North Houston Space Society, a chapter of National Space Society

**Tanveer Kathawalla**—Founder and former chief operating officer of Analytical Space, a satellite communications company based out of Boston that is leveraging hybrid RF-laser communications technology.

**Antonio Fowl Stark**—Space policy analyst and former Asia-Pacific regional partnerships manager at Space Generation Advisory Council, which holds Permanent Observer status at the United Nations Committee on the Peaceful Uses of Outer Space

I'd like to thank the individuals who supported my book:

Adya Rao
Alice Cho
Benjamin Kim
Bonnie LaBonte
Bridgette Han
ByungJun Kim
Candy Chan
Chiara Perotti Correa
Chloe Tan
Diana Davidson
Elizabeth Yang
Emily Green
Eric Koester
Eric Kwon
Gabrielle Villadolid
Hana Mamnoon
Heegook Yeo
Hochul Lee
Hoon Byun
Hyejin Kim
Hyun Kyung Kim
Im Hyun Jung
Isaac Benaka
Jaehyung Yoo
Jamie Hwang
Jasmine Park
Jisoo Chung
Ji Yoon Ahn
Jonathan Lee
Jordan Battaglia
Joo Chae Yeon

Alex Papadakis
Arielle Ostry
Bokyung Mun
Brian Choi
Brittani Chapman
Calvin T. Chung
Channing Lee
Chris Yang
Daniela Nemirovsky
Diana Davidson
Eliza Khokhar
Emily Isaac
Eum Boo Yeong
Francis Lee
Haeon Yoon
Harsh Dubey
Hee Jin Jang
Hohyun lee
Hoon Byun
Hyun Cheul Kim
Iksoo Jung
Iris Mak
Isabella Honora Thilmany
Jae Joo
Janeva Nicole Dimen
Jeiho Kim
Jisoo Chung
Jon Kaldan
Joohwan Park
Jordan Bolden
JooHee Julia Lee

Joo Yong Chul
Katherine Lee
Ken Kang
Kevin Zhen
Kim Jong Kil
Kim Tae Gun
Lauren Binnington
Leena Hamad
Lok Sang Andre Chan
Luz Lim
Mark Roh
Min Larson
Nagyon Kim
Nikki Sotak
Park Jun Young
Raul Galvan
Rui Lim
Sawatdii
Seungmin Han
Sidney Lee
Soo Bin Park
Stella Woo
Stephanie Pan
Sungho Parck
Vivi Nguyen
Woongjae Joo
Xinkai Zhou
Yoon Jong Hyeon
Yuen Yee Leung

Julie Chung
Kayla Lichtman
Ken Nguyen
Kim Hagseong
Kim Jongmin
Kyoko Okuyama
Lauren Wilson C
Lee Soyoung
Lynn Chong
Maegan Moriarty
Miléna DeGuere
MJ Jang
Nikki Perry
Park Il Bong
Qinthara Fatharani
Richard Sherwood
Samantha Savage
Sebin Song
Seungmin Park
Si Hyun Joo
Soon-Hyuk Lee
Stella Woo
Steven Vo
Teffanie Goh
Wendi Yan
Woo Seok Joo
Yeojin Kwon
Youngil Ko

I'd also like to thank the group of beta readers who supported my campaign and gave feedback on my writing: Teffanie Goh, Steven Kim, Luz Lim, Sidney Lee, and Haeon Yoon. Special thanks go to Jisoo Chung, my super beta reader and super friend, who has from the very beginning of my writing journey cheered me on, consistently provided constructive criticism, and helped me believe in myself in moments of doubt. I couldn't have written this book without you.

Thank you to my sister Caitlin Sihyun Joo, the talented artist who provided the artwork in this book. She painted "Venus," "Uranus," and "Mars" using gouache and watercolor when I told her I was writing a book about space, and she inspired me to write about the special relationship between our art and the universe.

No step of this journey would have been attainable without the great team at New Degree Press. I'm endlessly grateful for Eric Koester (founder of the Creator Institute) who convinced me I had grand, ingenious ideas, Aislyn Gilbert, the greatest development editor one could have asked for (thankfully we shared the same sense of humor), and to Chelsea Olivia, my amazing marketing and revisions editor, for steadily holding my hand until the end of this journey.

Special thanks goes out to: 엄마, 아빠. Thank you for everything you have gifted me. 전생에 세상을 구했나봐요. You have given me all the tools to fly, and through this book, I've flown across the furthest reaches of the universe. 사랑해요 엄마, 사랑해요 아빠.

Finally, thank you to my brother. You are the muse for my book and the reason I want to become a better writer, sister, and person. May you one day write a better book debunking all my points and get the last laugh.

made me smile!

# APPENDIX

## INTRODUCTION

*California Academy of Sciences.* "Science Today: Octomom of the Deep | California Academy of Sciences." August 29, 2014. Video, 3:02. https://www.youtube.com/watch?v=WhuuyhgZios.

Creighton, Jolene. "Scientists Discover Longest-Living and Longest-Brooding Octopus: Guards Eggs For 4.5 Years." Futurism. August 1, 2014. Accessed June 22, 2021. https://futurism.com/scientists-discover-longest-living-and-longest-brooding-octopus-guards-eggs-for-4-5-years.

Dorrian, Gareth. "The Four Most Promising Worlds for Alien Life in the Solar System." *The Conversation,* September 18, 2020. https://theconversation.com/the-four-most-promising-worlds-for-alien-life-in-the-solar-system-146358.

McEwen, Annie. "Octomom." May 15, 2020. In *Radiolab.* WNYC-STUDIOS. Podcast, MP3 audio, 28:10. https://www.wnycstudios.org/podcasts/radiolab/articles/octomom.

Sagan, Carl. *Cosmos*. New York: Random House, 2002.

## CHAPTER 1

Ali Akbar, Ahmed. "I Avoided 'Call of Duty: Modern Warfare' Because I Didn't Want to Be the Villain." *BuzzFeed News*, April 29, 2017. https://www.buzzfeednews.com/article/ahmedaliakbar/playing-call-of-duty-while-muslim.

Chao, Melody M., Donna J. Yao, and Franki Y. H. Kung. "Understanding the Divergent Effects of Multicultural Exposure." *International Journal of Intercultural Relations* 47 (2015): 78–88.

Clements, Ron, dir. *Aladdin*. 1992; Burbank, CA: Walt Disney Pictures.

Davis, Julie Hirschfeld. "Trump Calls Some Unauthorized Immigrants 'Animals' in Rant." *New York Times*, May 16, 2018. https://www.nytimes.com/2018/05/16/us/politics/trump-undocumented-immigrants-animals.html.

Frook, John Evan. "'Aladdin' Lyrics Altered." *Variety*, July 12, 1993. https://variety.com/1993/film/news/aladdin-lyrics-altered-108628/.

Gates, Henry Louis, Jr. "Scramble for Africa." Oxford Reference. Accessed June 25, 2021. https://www.oxfordreference.com/view/10.1093/acref/9780195337709.001.0001/acref-9780195337709-e-3500.

Grossman, Dave. *On Killing: The Psychological Cost of Learning to Kill in War and Society*. New York: Back Bay Books, 2009.

Ichioka, Yuji. "Japanese Immigrant Response to the 1920 Alien Land Law." *Agricultural History* 58 (1984): 157–78.

Lee, Nicole. "Shooting the Arabs: How Video Games Perpetuate Muslim Stereotypes." *Engadget,* March 24, 2016. https://www.engadget.com/2016-03-24-shooting-the-arabs-how-video-games-perpetuate-muslim-stereotype.html.

Mann, Charles C. *1491: New Revelations of the Americas before Columbus.* New York: Alfred A. Knopf, 2019.

Menken, Alan, composer. *Aladdin: Original Motion Picture Soundtrack.* Walt Disney Records, 1992, compact disc.

Moffat, Robert. *The Matabele Journals of Robert Moffat.* Salisbury: National Archives of Rhodesia, 1976.

The Observers-France. "Video: Palestinian Woman Shot and Killed by Israeli Soldiers at Checkpoint." The Observers—France 24. September 20, 2019. https://observers.france24.com/en/20190920-palestinian-woman-shot-killed-israeli-soldiers-checkpoint.

Olin, Spencer C. "European Immigrant and Oriental Alien: Acceptance and Rejection by the California Legislature of 1913." *Pacific Historical Review* 35, no. 3 (1966): 303–15. Accessed June 25, 2021. doi:10.2307/3636790.

Romaniuk, Scott, and Tobias Burgers. "How the US Military Is Using 'Violent, Chaotic, Beautiful' Video Games to Train Soldiers." The Conversation. November 20, 2020. Accessed June 28, 2021. https://theconversation.com/how-the-us-military-is-using-violent-chaotic-beautiful-video-games-to-train-soldiers-73826.

Sohn, Stephen Hong. "Introduction: Alien/Asian: Imagining the Racialized Future." *MELUS* 33, no. 4 (2008): 5–22. Accessed June 25, 2021. http://www.jstor.org/stable/20343505.

Stangarone, Troy. 2011. "South Korea's Arab Spring Role?" *The Diplomat*, October 21, 2011. https://thediplomat.com/2011/10/south-koreas-arab-spring-role/.

Thomas, Thomas Morgan. *Eleven Years in Central South Africa*. London: Cass, 1971.

## CHAPTER 2

Adams, Carol J. *The Sexual Politics of Meat: A Feminist-Vegetarian Critical Theory*. New York; London: Bloomsbury, 2019.

Anthony, David W. *The Horse, the Wheel and Language: How Bronze-Age Riders from the Eurasian Steppes Shaped the Modern World*. Princeton: Princeton University Press, 2010.

Augé, Marc, and Amy Jacobs. *A Sense for the Other: The Timeliness and Relevance of Anthropology*. Stanford: Stanford University Press, 1998.

Boesch, Christophe. *Away from Ethnocentrism and Anthropocentrism: Towards a Scientific Understanding of "What Makes Us Human."* Cambridge Journals. 2010. https://www.eva.mpg.de/documents/Cambridge/Boesch_Ethnocentrism_BehBrainSci_2010_1552709.pdf.

Cameron, James, dir. *Avatar.* 2009; Beverly Hills, CA: Twentieth Century Fox, 2010. DVD.

"Definition of Veganism." The Vegan Society. Accessed June 25, 2021. https://www.vegansociety.com/go-vegan/definition-veganism.

Denning, Kathryn. *How Humans Matter Now: The Relevances of Anthropology and Archaeology for the New SETI. [White paper for SETI Institute call 2017],* Academia. 2017. Accessed April 20, 2020. https://www.academia.edu/36288634/How_Humans_Matter_Now_The_Relevances_of_Anthropology_and_Archaeology_for_the_New_SETI_White_paper_for_SETI_Institute_call_2017_.

Goldberg, Eric, and Mike Gabriel, dirs. *Pocahontas.* 1995; United States: Buena Vista Pictures.

Ilian, George. *Warren Buffett: The Life and Business Lessons of Warren Buffett.* 2016.

Maybury-Lewis, David. *Millennium: Tribal Wisdom and the Modern World.* Toronto: Penguin, 1993.

NASA Goddard Space Flight Center. "Honey Bee Net." Accessed May 9, 2021. https://honeybeenet.gsfc.nasa.gov/index.htm.

Santayana, George. *The Life of Reason.* United States: Echo Library, 2006.

Shipman, Pat. *The Invaders: How Humans and Their Dogs Drove Neanderthals to Extinction.* Cambridge: Belknap Press of Harvard University Press, 2017.

University of Kentucky College of Arts & Sciences. "Horse Whispers: How Linguistics Illustrates the History of Horses." Accessed May 9, 2021. https://linguistics.as.uky.edu/horse-whispers-how-linguistics-illustrates-history-horses.

Wang, G., W. Zhai, et al. "The Genomics of Selection in Dogs and the Parallel Evolution between Dogs and Humans." *Nature Communications* 4 (2013): 1860. DOI:10.1038/ncomms2814.

Yale University's School of Forestry and Environmental Studies. "Cattle Ranching in the Amazon Region | Global Forest Atlas." 2020. https://globalforestatlas.yale.edu/amazon/land-use/cattle-ranching.

## CHAPTER 3

Abrams, J. J., dir. *Star Trek.* 2-disc digital copy special ed. Hollywood, CA: Paramount Home Entertainment, 2009. DVD.

Anthony, David W. *The Horse, The Wheel, and Language: How Bronze-Age Riders from the Eurasian Steppes Shaped the Modern World.* Princeton: Princeton University Press, 2007.

Augé, Marc, and Amy Jacobs. *A Sense for the Other: The Timeliness and Relevance of Anthropology.* Stanford: Stanford University Press, 1998.

Bowerman, Mary. "Stephen Hawking: If Aliens Call, We Should Be 'Wary of Answering.'" *USA TODAY,* September 23, 2016. https://www.usatoday.com/story/tech/nation-now/2016/09/23/stephen-hawking-aliens-wary-answering-back-intelligent-life/90895018/.

Catling, David. *Astrobiology: A Very Short Introduction.* Oxford University Press, 2014.

Cuarón, Alfonso, dir. *Gravity.* 2013; Burbank, CA: Warner Bros. Pictures, 2014. Blu-ray Disc, 1080p HD.

Francione, Gary L., and Anna E. Charlton. "Why Keeping a Pet Is Fundamentally Unethical—Gary L Francione & Anna E Charlton: Aeon Essays." Aeon. September 8, 2016. Accessed June 25, 2021. https://aeon.co/essays/why-keeping-a-pet-is-fundamentally-unethical.

Jackson, Katrina Marie. "The Influence of Television and Film on Interest in Space and Science." (master's thesis, University of North Dakota, 2013). 1438. https://commons.und.edu/theses/1438.

Leinfelder, Andrea. "Why One Houston-Area Man Asked about the Moon Every Day for a Year." *Houston Chronicle,* December 20, 2020. Accessed May 30, 2021. https://www.houstonchronicle.com/news/houston-texas/space/article/His-daily-query-for-a-year-Did-you-know-NASA-is-15807786.php?utm_campaign=CMS Sharing Tools (Premium)&utm_source=t.co&utm_medium=referral#photo-20392920.

Maybury-Lewis, David. *Millennium: Tribal Wisdom and the Modern World.* Toronto: Penguin, 1993.

Roddenberry, Gene, Gene L. Coon, John Meredyth Lucas, Margaret Armen, Jerome Bixby, Robert Bloch, Max Ehrlich, et al. *Star trek, the original series.* 2008.

Scott, Ridley, dir. *The Martian*. Los Angeles, CA: 20th Century Fox, 2015.

Shipman, P. *The Invaders: How Humans and their Dogs Drove Neanderthals to Extinction*. Cambridge: Belknap Press of Harvard University Press, 2015.

TED. "9 TED Talks on Overcoming Fear." Playlists. Watch. Accessed May 28, 2021. https://www.ted.com/playlists/468/how_to_overcome_your_fears.

Vakoch, Douglas A. *Psychology of Space Exploration: Contemporary Research in Historical Perspective*. Washington, DC: National Aeronautics and Space Administration, 2011.

Wang, G., W. Zhai, et al. The Genomics of Selection in Dogs and the Parallel Evolution between Dogs and Humans. *Nature Communications* 4 (2013): 1860. DOI:10.1038/ncomms2814.

White, Frank. *The Overview Effect: Space Exploration and Human Evolution*. Reston: American Institute of Aeronautics and Astronautics, 2014.

Wells, H. G. *The War of the Worlds*. New York: Dover Publications, 1997.

Yaden, David B., Jonathan Iwry, Kelley J. Slack, Johannes C. Eichstaedt, Yukun Zhao, George E. Vaillant, and Andrew B. Newberg. "The Overview Effect: Awe and Self-Transcendent Experience in Space Flight." *Psychology of Consciousness: Theory, Research, and Practice* 3, no. 1 (2016): 1–11. doi:10.1037/cns0000086.

## CHAPTER 4

Chang, Kenneth, Dennis Overbye, and Shannon Stirone. "Life on Venus? Astronomers See a Signal in Its Clouds." *New York Times,* September 14, 2020. https://www.nytimes.com/2020/09/14/science/venus-life-clouds.html.

David, Leonard. "Will 2020 Be the Year We Find Intelligent Alien Life?" *Space.com,* November 25, 2019. https://www.space.com/will-alien-life-be-found-2020.html.

Dunbar, Brian. "Voyage to Vaccine Discovery Continues with Space Station Salmonella Study." NASA. Accessed June 26, 2021. https://www.nasa.gov/mission_pages/station/research/news/RASV.html.

Guarino, Ben. "'First Protest in Space' Targets Trump with an Astronaut's Famous Words." *Washington Post,* April 29, 2019. Accessed June 25, 2021. https://www.washingtonpost.com/news/speaking-of-science/wp/2017/04/14/first-protest-in-space-targets-trump-with-an-astronauts-famous-words/.

"List of Astronauts by Year of Selection." National Aeronautics and Space Administration Wiki. Accessed June 08, 2021. https://nasa.fandom.com/wiki/List_of_astronauts_by_year_of_selection.

Loff, Sarah. "Artemis Program." NASA. June 04, 2019. Accessed May 22, 2021. https://www.nasa.gov/artemisprogram/.

Lutz, Eleanor. "20 Years Aboard the International Space Station." *New York Times,* November 2, 2020. Accessed May 29, 2021.

https://www.nytimes.com/interactive/2020/11/02/science/iss-20th-anniversary-timeline.html.

Mahoney, Erin. "NASA Selects Blue Origin, Dynetics, SpaceX for Artemis Human Landers." NASA. April 30, 2020. Accessed May 22, 2021. https://www.nasa.gov/feature/nasa-selects-blue-origin-dynetics-spacex-for-artemis-human-landers.

Majowicz, Shannon E., Jennie Musto, Elaine Scallan, Frederick J. Angulo, Martyn Kirk, Sarah J. O'Brien, Timothy F. Jones, Aamir Fazil, and Robert M. Hoekstra. "Global Burden of Nontyphoidal Salmonella Gastroenteritis." OUP Academic. March 15, 2010. Accessed June 26, 2021. https://academic.oup.com/cid/article/50/6/882/419872.

Naskar, Abhijit. *Saint of The Sapiens.* CreateSpace Independent Publishing Platform, 2018.

Price, Nathan. "Countdown to the Moon." *Nathan Price* (blog). https://www.countdowntothemoon.org/.

Price, Nathan. "NSS North Houston Space Society." *NSS North Houston Space Society* (blog). https://www.northhoustonspace.org/

Riess, Helen. "The Science of Empathy." *Journal of Patient Experience* 4, 2 (2017): 74–77. doi:10.1177/2374373517699267

Siegel, Ethan. "Why Exploring Space and Investing in Research Is Non-Negotiable." Forbes. October 26, 2017. Accessed May 23, 2021. https://www.forbes.com/sites/startswithabang/2017/10/26/even-while-the-world-suffers-investing-in-science-is-non-negotiable/?sh=142af4651647.

Wood, Betty. "NASA Backs Designs for 3D-printed Homes on Mars." The Spaces. July 30, 2018. Accessed June 26, 2021. https://thespaces.com/ai-space-factory-designs-homes-for-planet-mars/.

## CHAPTER 5

Burnett, James H., III. "Racism Learned—The Boston Globe." BostonGlobe.com. June 10, 2012. Accessed June 28, 2021. https://www.bostonglobe.com/business/2012/06/09/harvard-researcher-says-children-learn-racism-quickly/gWuN1ZG3M40WihER2kAfdK/story.html.

Chen, Jeffrey C. J. "How Star Wars Reinforces Our Prejudices." *Washington Post*, December 23, 2019. Accessed May 22, 2020. https://www.washingtonpost.com/outlook/2019/12/23/how-star-wars-reinforces-our-prejudices/.

David, E. J. R., Tiera M. Schroeder, and Jessicaanne Fernandez. "Internalized Racism: A Systematic Review of the Psychological Literature on Racism's Most Insidious Consequence." *Journal of Social Issues* 75 (2019): 1057–1086. https://doi.org/10.1111/josi.12350".

Klein, Ezra. "Obama Explains How America Went From 'Yes We Can' to 'MAGA.'" *The Ezra Klein Show*, June 1, 2021. Accessed June 5, 2021. https://www.nytimes.com/2021/06/01/opinion/ezra-klein-podcast-barack-obama.html.

Kant, Immanuel. *Perpetual Peace; A Philosophical Essay*, 1795. London: S. Sonnenschein, 1903.

Irving, Henry. "Invasion Publicity during the Second World War." History of Government. June 18, 2015. Accessed May 28, 2021. https://history.blog.gov.uk/2015/06/18/invasion-publicity-during-the-second-world-war/.

## CHAPTER 6

Ban, Ki-Moon. "Remarks at Stanford University Secretary-General." United Nations. January 17, 2013. Accessed May 31, 2021. https://www.un.org/sg/en/content/sg/speeches/2013-01-17/remarks-stanford-university.

Devlin, Kat. "Unlike in US, Most European Students Learn a Foreign Language." Pew Research Center. March 13, 2021. Accessed May 31, 2021. https://www.pewresearch.org/fact-tank/2018/08/06/most-european-students-are-learning-a-foreign-language-in-school-while-americans-lag/.

*Encyclopædia Britannica.* "The Age of Discovery." Accessed June 5, 2021. https://www.britannica.com/topic/European-exploration/The-Age-of-Discovery.

Ethnologue. "How Many Languages Are There in the World?" February 23, 2021. Accessed June 27, 2021. https://www.ethnologue.com/guides/how-many-languages.

Fan, Samantha P., Zoe Liberman, Boaz Keysar, and Katherine D. Kinzler. "The Exposure Advantage: Early Exposure to a Multilingual Environment Promotes Effective Communication." *Psychological Science* 26, no. 7 (July 2015): 1090–97. https://doi.org/10.1177/0956797615574699.

Farley, David. "Travel—The Truth about Japanese Tempura." *BBC*, August 10, 2017. Accessed May 31, 2021. http://www.bbc.com/travel/story/20170808-the-truth-about-japanese-tempura.

Gore, Al. "What We Should Remember Today and Every Day: We Share Mother Earth as Our Only Home. There Is No Planet B. Happy #EarthDay Everyone! Beautiful Photo Courtesy of @NASA's #DSCOVR Satellite. Pic.twitter.com/f8XLjZjq4C." Twitter. April 22, 2019. Accessed May 31, 2021. https://twitter.com/algore/status/1120334916028370945?lang=en.

Johnson, Steven. "Colleges Lose a 'Stunning' 651 Foreign-Language Programs in 3 Years." The Chronicle of Higher Education. July 23, 2020. Accessed May 31, 2021. https://www.chronicle.com/article/Colleges-Lose-a-Stunning-/245526.

Keysar, Boaz, Sayuri L. Hayakawa, and Sun Gyu An. "The Foreign-Language Effect: Thinking in a Foreign Tongue Reduces Decision Biases." *Psychological Science* 23, 6 (2012): 661–668. doi:10.1177/0956797611432178.

Kobayashi, Yoko. "Europe versus Asia: Foreign Language Education Other than English in Japan's Higher Education." *Higher Education* 66 (2013). 10.1007/s10734-012-9603-7.

Kono, Akira. "Portuguese-Japanese Language Contact in 16th Century Japan." *Bulletin of Portuguese—Japanese Studies* 3 (2001): 43–51. Redalyc, https://www.redalyc.org/articulo.oa?id=36100304.

Lidin, Olof G. *Tanegashima: The Arrival of Europe in Japan.* Copenhagen: NIAS Press, 2004.

McKell, Kaleena. "Foreign Language Demand Growing." The Daily Universe. March 27, 2018. Accessed May 31, 2021. https://universe.byu.edu/2018/03/27/foreign-language-demand-growing1/.

McWhorter, John. "Why the Words for 'Mom' and 'Dad' Sound So Similar in So Many Languages." The Atlantic. October 12, 2015. Accessed May 31, 2021. https://www.theatlantic.com/international/archive/2015/10/words-mom-dad-similar-languages/409810/.

Morita, Takeshi. *Nippo Jisho*. Tokyo: Iwanami Shoten, 1961.

Payne, Thomas E. *Describing Morphosyntax: A Guide for Field Linguists*. Cambridge: Cambridge University Press, 1997.

Reporters, Telegraph. "Why Learn a Foreign Language? The Benefits of Bilingualism." The Telegraph. March 27, 2018. Accessed May 31, 2021. https://www.telegraph.co.uk/education/2018/03/27/learn-foreign-language-benefits-bilingualism/.

Russo, Anthony, and Joe Russo, dirs. *Avengers: Endgame*. Burbank, CA: Walt Disney Studios Motion Pictures, 2019.

Vande, Walle, and Willy F. "The Language Barrier in the History of Japanese-European Relations." March 1996. doi/10.15055/00003569.

Vince, Gaia. "The Amazing Benefits of Being Bilingual." BBC Future. August 13, 2016. Accessed May 31, 2021. https://www.bbc.com/future/article/20160811-the-amazing-benefits-of-being-bilingual.

Welle, Deutsche. "'Avengers: Endgame' Beats 'Avatar' to Become Highest-Grossing Movie Ever: DW: 22.07.2019." DW.COM. Accessed June 5, 2021. https://www.dw.com/en/avengers-endgame-beats-avatar-to-become-highest-grossing-movie-ever/a-49688980.

## CHAPTER 7

"Art as Cultural Diplomacy." Academy for Cultural Diplomacy. Accessed June 7, 2021. https://www.culturaldiplomacy.org/academy/index.php?en_acd_about.

Bjerklie, Sarah George. "Why Food Is a Huge Part of Diplomacy, According to Ambassadors." Spoon University. May 12, 2016. Accessed June 7, 2021. https://spoonuniversity.com/lifestyle/why-food-is-a-huge-part-of-diplomacy-according-to-ambassadors.

Cha, Victor. "The World Cup and Sports Diplomacy." *Comparative Connections* 4, no. 2 (June 2002). Accessed June 7, 2021. http://cc.pacforum.org/2002/07/world-cup-sports-diplomacy/.

Denning, Kathryn. *How Humans Matter Now: The Relevances of Anthropology and Archaeology for the New SETI. [White paper for SETI Institute call 2017]*, Academia. 2017. Accessed, April 20, 2020.

Ferreira, Becky. "Chris Hadfield's Spirited Song in Space Was No "oddity." *New York Times,* November 2, 2020. Accessed June 21, 2021. https://www.nytimes.com/2020/11/02/science/chris-hadfield-space-oddity.html.

Greicius, Tony. "NASA Spacecraft Embarks on Historic Journey into Interstellar Space." *NASA*, September 12, 2013. www.nasa.gov/mission_pages/voyager/voyager20130912.html.

Hadfield, Chirs. "Space Oddity." Chris Hadfield. Accessed June 21, 2021. https://chrishadfield.ca/space-oddity/.

MasterClass. "New Age Music Guide: A Brief History of New Age Music—2021." MasterClass. April 30, 2021. Accessed June 7, 2021. https://www.masterclass.com/articles/new-age-music-guide#a-brief-history-of-new-age-music.

Mintz, Steven. "The Gilder Lehrman Institute of American History." Historical Context: Facts about the Slave Trade and Slavery | Gilder Lehrman Institute of American History. Accessed June 25, 2021. https://www.gilderlehrman.org/history-resources/teaching-resource/historical-context-facts-about-slave-trade-and-slavery.

Morgan, Morris H., Alexander Agassiz, and Edward C. Pickering. "The Constellation Camelopardalis." *Harvard College Observatory Circular* 146 (December 1908): 1–3.

NASA. "Voyager 1 Has Entered Interstellar Space." *NASA*, September 12, 2013. www.jpl.nasa.gov/news/news.php?release=2013-278.

NASA. "Voyager—Images on the Golden Record." *NASA*. Accessed June 7, 2021. https://voyager.jpl.nasa.gov/galleries/images-on-the-golden-record/.

Nelson, Jon. "Voyager—The Golden Record." NASA Jet Propulsion Laboratory California Institute of Technology | Voyager. Accessed June 7, 2021. voyager.jpl.nasa.gov/golden-record/ (http://voyager.jpl.nasa.gov/golden-record/).

*Oxford English Dictionary*. s.v. "Culture." Accessed June 7, 2021. https://www.oxfordlearnersdictionaries.com/definition/english/culture_1?q=culture.

"North Korea: UN Commission Documents Wide-Ranging and Ongoing Crimes against Humanity, Urges Referral to ICC." OHCHR. February 17, 2014. Accessed June 7, 2021. https://www.ohchr.org/en/NewsEvents/Pages/DisplayNews.aspx?NewsID=14255&LangID=E.

Smyth, David. "Lady Gagas Chromatica Is a Non-Stop Pop Rocket into Space." London Evening Standard | Evening Standard, May 29, 2020. Accessed June 7, 2021. https://www.standard.co.uk/culture/music/lady-gaga-chromatica-review-new-album-a4454006.html.

Suntikul, Wantanee. "BTS and the Global Spread of Korean Soft Power." The Diplomat. March 4, 2019. Accessed June 7, 2021. https://thediplomat.com/2019/03/bts-and-the-global-spread-of-korean-soft-power/.

Vandenberg, Layne. "Sports Diplomacy: The Case of the Two Koreas." The Diplomat. October 10, 2019. Accessed June 7, 2021. https://thediplomat.com/2019/10/sports-diplomacy-the-case-of-the-two-koreas/.

Webster, Emma, Matt Brennan, Adam Behr, Martin Cloonan, and Jake Ansell. "Valuing Live Music: The UK Live Music Census 2017 Report." UK Live Music Census, February 2018. http://uklivemusiccensus.org/wp-content/uploads/2018/03/UK-Live-Music-Census-2017-full-report.pdf.

Weiner, Ken. "Can AI Create True Art?" Scientific American Blog Network. November 12, 2018. Accessed June 7, 2021. https://blogs.scientificamerican.com/observations/can-ai-create-true-art/.

Widdicombe, Lizzie. "The End of Food." The New Yorker. May 5, 2014. Accessed June 7, 2021. https://www.newyorker.com/magazine/2014/05/12/the-end-of-food.

Yonhap. "BTS Songs to Hit Playlist of NASA's Next Lunar Journey." *The Korea Herald,* June 7, 2019. Accessed June 7, 2021. http://www.koreaherald.com/view.php?ud=20190607000347.

## CHAPTER 8

Andersen, Ross. "Elon Musk Puts His Case for a Multi-Planet Civilisation—Ross Andersen: Aeon Essays." Aeon. September 30, 2014. Accessed June 12, 2021. https://aeon.co/essays/elon-musk-puts-his-case-for-a-multi-planet-civilisation.

AP The Associated Press. "Armstrong's Famous 'One Small Step' Quote—Explained." Navy Times. July 13, 2019. Accessed June 12, 2021. https://www.navytimes.com/news/your-navy/2019/07/13/armstrongs-famous-one-small-step-quote-explained/.

ArcGIS. "Story Map Tour." Arcgis.com. Accessed June 11, 2021. https://www.arcgis.com/apps/MapTour/index.html?appid=09bad7b2f1c3418b9c381749a006092e.

Bartenstein, Kristin. "Flag-Planting: What Legal Framework Governs the Division of the Arctic Continental Shelf?" *International Journal* 65, no. 1 (2009): 187–206. Accessed June 11, 2021. http://www.jstor.org/stable/25681093.

Collins, Michael. *Carrying the Fire.* New York: Farrar, Straus Giroux, 2009.

Courage, Alexander and Gene Roddenberry. "Star Trek (Ft. William Shatner)—Star Trek Opening." Genius. Accessed June 12, 2021. https://genius.com/Star-trek-star-trek-opening-lyrics.

Davenport, Christian. "The Biden Administration Has Set out to Dismantle Trump's Legacy, except in One Area: Space." *Washington Post,* March 2, 2021. Accessed June 26, 2021. https://www.washingtonpost.com/technology/2021/03/02/biden-space-artemis-moon-trump/.

Ennis, Simon. "'The Man Who Sells the Moon.'" *New York Times,* March 11, 2013. Accessed June 12, 2021. https://www.nytimes.com/2013/03/11/opinion/the-man-who-sells-the-moon.html.

ESA. "ESA Turns 30! A Successful Track Record for Europe in Space." ESA. May 31, 2005. Accessed June 12, 2021. https://www.esa.int/Newsroom/Press_Releases/ESA_turns_30!_A_successful_track_record_for_Europe_in_space.

Farnham, Alan. "For Sale: Acre Lots on Moon with Earth View, $19.99." *ABC News*, May 1, 2013. Accessed June 12, 2021. https://abcnews.go.com/Business/sale-real-estate-moon/story?id=19068377.

Hambleton, Kathryn. "Artemis Partners." NASA. January 16, 2020. Accessed June 12, 2021. https://www.nasa.gov/content/artemis-partners.

Hern, Alex. "The Tech Billionaire Space Race: Who Is Jeff Bezos up Against?" *The Guardian,* June 7, 2021. Accessed June 12, 2021. https://www.theguardian.com/science/2021/jun/07/the-tech-billionaire-space-race-who-is-jeff-bezos-up-against.

Kluger, Jeffrey. "A Biden Presidency Might Slow the US in the Space Race." Time. November 10, 2020. Accessed June 26, 2021. https://time.com/5907796/biden-space-program/.

Leib, Karl. "International Competition and Ideology in US Space Policy." *International Studies Notes* 24, no. 3 (1999): 30–45. Accessed June 11, 2021. http://www.jstor.org/stable/44235351.

M.b., Dastagiri. "The Theory and Economics of MARS and MOON Colonization: Steps and Policy Advocacy." *European Scientific Journal, ESJ* 13, no. 28 (2017): 239. doi:10.19044/esj.2017.v13n28p239.

Miller, Robert J. *Native America, Discovered and Conquered: Thomas Jefferson, Lewis & Clark, and Manifest Destiny.* Lincoln: University of Nebraska Press, 2008.

Mosher, Dave. "The American Flags Astronauts Planted on the Moon Are Disintegrating." *Business Insider*, July 10, 2019.

Accessed June 21, 2021. https://www.businessinsider.com/american-flags-moon-color-bleached-white-2017-4.

Mosher, Dave. "'We Want Our Country to Do It First': A NASA Executive Says a US-China Mars Mission Is Not in the Cards." *Business Insider,* August 17, 2019. Accessed June 12, 2021. https://www.businessinsider.com/nasa-china-why-no-joint-human-mars-mission-2019–7.

Platoff, Anne M. "Where No Flag Has Gone Before." NASA. August 1993. Accessed June 11, 2021. https://www.hq.nasa.gov/alsj/alsj-usflag.html#FN7.

Pullis, Jacob H. "Star Trek as an Agent of Cultural Reproduction." (Senior thesis, Trinity College, Hartford, CT, 2014.) Trinity College Digital Repository, https://digitalrepository.trincoll.edu/theses/397.

Roddenberry, Gene, Marc Daniels, William Shatner, Leonard Nimoy, DeForest Kelley, James Doohan, George Takei, and Alexander Courage. *Star Trek, The Original Series. Season One.* Hollywood, CA: Paramount, 2004.

Sandefur, Timothy. "The Politics of Star Trek." Claremont Review of Books. 2015. Accessed June 12, 2021. https://claremontreviewofbooks.com/the-politics-of-star-trek/.

Sarantakes, Nicholas Evan. "Cold War Pop Culture and the Image of US Foreign Policy: The Perspective of the Original Star Trek Series." *Journal of Cold War Studies* 7, no. 4 (October 1, 2005): 74–103. https://doi.org/10.1162/1520397055012488.

Simmons, Roger. "Apollo Facts: 11 Things You Probably Don't Know about the Moon Mission." *American Military News*, July 3, 2019. Accessed June 11, 2021. https://americanmilitarynews.com/2019/07/apollo-facts-11-things-you-probably-dont-know-about-the-moon-mission/.

Werth, Karsten. "A Surrogate for War—The US Space Program in the 1960s." *Amerikastudien / American Studies* 49, no. 4 (2004): 563–87. Accessed June 11, 2021. http://www.jstor.org/stable/41158096.

## CHAPTER 9

Chang, Kenneth, Dennis Overbye, and Shannon Stirone. "Life on Venus? Astronomers See a Signal in Its Clouds." *New York Times*, September 14, 2020. https://www.nytimes.com/2020/09/14/science/venus-life-clouds.html.

Corey, James, Hallie Lambert, and Georgia Lee. *The Expanse*. Los Angeles, CA: Boom! Studios, 2018.

Favreau, Jon. *Iron Man*. United States: Paramount Pictures, 2008.

Harwood, William. "Unidentified Bidder Pays $28 Million in Auction to Join Bezos for July Space Flight." *CBS News*, June 12, 2021. Accessed June 16, 2021. https://www.cbsnews.com/news/jeff-bezos-auction-blue-origin-28-million-rocket-new-shephard-spaceflight/.

HBO Entertainment; co-executive producers, George R.R. Martin, Vince Gerardis, Ralph Vicinanza, Guymon Casady, Carolyn Strauss; producers, Mark Huffam, Frank Doelger; executive producers David Benioff, D.B. Weiss; created by David Benioff & D.B. Weiss; Television 360; Grok! Television; Generator Entertainment; Bighead Littlehead. *Game of Thrones. The Complete First Season.* New York: HBO Home Entertainment, 2012.

Landfester, Ulrike, Nina-Louisa Remuss, Kai-Uwe Schrogl, and Jean-Claude Worms. "SETI's Declaration of Principles Concerning Activities Following the Detection of Extraterrestrial Intelligence." In *Humans in Outer Space—Interdisciplinary Perspectives*, edited by Ulrike Landfester, Nina-Louisa Remuss, Kai-Uwe Schrogl, and Jean-Claude Worms. *Studies in Space Policy* 5 (2011). Springer, Vienna. https://doi.org/10.1007/978-3-7091-0280-0_22.

Lee, Chung Min. "A Peninsula of Paradoxes: South Korean Public Opinion on Unification and Outside Powers." Carnegie Endowment for International Peace. May 13, 2020. Accessed June 17, 2021. https://carnegieendowment.org/2020/05/13/peninsula-of-paradoxes-south-korean-public-opinion-on-unification-and-outside-powers-pub-81737.

Nam, Kwangsik. "Today in Korean History." Yonhap News Agency. June 17, 2021. Accessed June 21, 2021. https://en.yna.co.kr/view/AEN20210617003400320.

O'Neill, Mike. "Space Junk and Human Spacecraft—Department of Defense Tracking More Than 27,000 Pieces of Orbital Debris." SciTechDaily. June 3, 2021. Accessed June 16, 2021. https://scitechdaily.com/space-junk-and-human-spacecraft-department-of-defense-tracking-more-than-27000-pieces-of-orbital-debris/.

SETI Permanent Study Group of the International Academy of Astronautics. "Declaration of Principles Concerning the Conduct of the Search for Extraterrestrial Intelligence." September 30, 2010. https://www.seti.org/protocols-eti-signal-detection.

## CHAPTER 10

"A Scientific Tour Of The Mysterious 'Dark Universe': NPR." Interview. *Morning Edition* (audio blog), October 31, 2013. Accessed June 17, 2021. https://www.npr.org/templates/story/story.php?storyId=242028462.

Global Optimism. "Team." February 10, 2021. Accessed June 27, 2021. https://globaloptimism.com/team/.

McMahon, Jeff. "10 Things You Can Do about Climate Change, According to the Shepherds of the Paris Agreement." Forbes. February 25, 2020. Accessed June 27, 2021. https://www.forbes.com/sites/jeffmcmahon/2020/02/25/10-things-you-can-do-about-climate-change-starting-in-your-head/?sh=60a7549d6f3c.

O'Neill, Mike. "Hidden Dark Forces: A New Dimension in the Quest to Understand Dark Matter." SciTechDaily. June 05, 2021. Accessed June 17, 2021. https://scitechdaily.com/hidden-dark-forces-a-new-dimension-in-the-quest-to-understand-dark-matter/.

Steffen, Alex, and Carissa Bluestone. *Worldchanging: A Users Guide for the 21st Century.* New York: Abrams, 2011.

Tolkien, J. R. R. *The Lord of the Rings.* London: HarperCollins, 1991.

## CHAPTER 11

Dunbar, Brian. "Oceans: The Great Unknown." NASA. October 8, 2009. Accessed June 21, 2021. https://www.nasa.gov/audience/forstudents/5-8/features/oceans-the-great-unknown-58.html.

Helmore, Edward. "Sold! Bidder Pays $28m for Spare Seat on Space Flight with Jeff Bezos." *The Guardian*, June 12, 2021. Accessed June 20, 2021. https://www.theguardian.com/science/2021/jun/12/jeff-bezos-space-auction-28m-spare-seat-blue-origin.

Letzter, Rafi. "9 Epic Space Discoveries You May Have Missed in 2020." LiveScience. January 2, 2021. Accessed June 20, 2021. https://www.livescience.com/epic-space-discoveries-of-2020.html.

McEwen, Annie. "Octomom." May 15, 2020. In *Radiolab*. WNYC-STUDIOS. Podcast, MP3 audio, 28:10. https://www.wnycstudios.org/podcasts/radiolab/articles/octomom.

Northon, Karen. "NASA Missions Provide New Insights into 'Ocean Worlds'." NASA. April 13, 2017. Accessed June 20, 2021. https://www.nasa.gov/press-release/nasa-missions-provide-new-insights-into-ocean-worlds-in-our-solar-system/.

US Department of Commerce, National Oceanic and Atmospheric Administration. "How Much of the Ocean Have We Explored?" NOAA's National Ocean Service. January 1, 2009. Accessed June 20, 2021. https://oceanservice.noaa.gov/facts/exploration.html.

US Department of Commerce, National Oceanic and Atmospheric Administration. "SUBSEA (Systematic Underwater Biogeochemical Science and Exploration Analog)." NOAA Office of Ocean Exploration and Research. August 21, 2018. Accessed June 20, 2021. https://oceanexplorer.noaa.gov/explorations/18subsea/welcome.html.

Made in the USA
Coppell, TX
11 September 2021